Coming Home To Ourselves

Journaling To Wholeness

Jan Forrest

To Sandy —
abundant blessings!
In Spirit —
Jan Forrest

Heart To Heart Press

Published by Heart To Heart Press, P.O. Box 215, West Olive, Michigan 49460.

Editor: Tracy McCasey
Cover Art and Design: Bonnie Herman Zachary
Composition: Laura Bedford and A.S.A.P. Transcriptions
Book Production: Eerdmans Printing

ISBN: 0-9663602-0-6

Manufactured in the United States of America.

Dedication

This book is lovingly dedicated to all the wonderful, wise women I have been fortunate enough to meet in my lifetime. Your courage and dedication to your own growth have fortified me on my journey more than you can imagine. Namasté.

About The Cover

The cover illustration is loosely based on Botticelli's famous painting "The Birth of Venus." In the original, Venus emerges from the depths of the sea. She appears gentle and unassuming, modestly covering her more feminine attributes with her long hair. To the Greeks, Venus (Aphrodite to the Romans) was the epitome of womanhood. She was the goddess of love and beauty, reigning supreme over feminine mysteries, as well as the arts of sculpture, poetry and music.

In this new artistic rendering, we have taken the liberty to update her image, creating a new Venus for the Modern Age. She emerges from the depth of her personal journey having created a new sense of self. She joyously dances on her shell, hair flowing, arms outstretched.

The heart with the atom symbolizes the atom that lies within each of us; the atom that contains all our memories of who we are. That atom lies in the center of our heart. The new Venus is opening up her heart to the energy of the Universe. She is remembering who she is. She is coming home to herself.

Jan Forrest
Bonnie Herman Zachary

And the day came when the risk to remain

tight in a bud was more painful than

the risk it took to blossom.

Anais Nin

Table of Contents

BEGINNING THE JOURNEY			1
CHAPTER 1	**LEARNING TO SELF-NURTURE: BEGINNING A PROGRAM OF SELF CARE**		7
	Filling Our Own Wells	7	
	Assessing Your Current Ability to Nurture Yourself	8	
	Self-Aware Versus Selfish	10	
	Giving Yourself Permission	12	
	Giving Up Perfection	12	
	Prioritizing For Personal Time	14	
	Being Passionate About "Me" Time	16	
CHAPTER 2	**GETTING STARTED**		19
	Creating Balance in Life	19	
	Journaling to Wholeness	21	
CHAPTER 3	**NURTURE YOUR BODY**		25
	Eating Healthfully for Longevity	27	
	Movement for Longevity	29	
	Movement for Spiritual Practice	31	
	Fine Tuning with Yoga	33	
	Breathing for Life	34	
	Creating "Island" Time	37	
	Self-Nourishing Rituals	39	
	Creating Healing Space	40	
	Loving Touch	42	
	Poem: "Doorways"	45	
	Journaling Pages: Body Messages	47	

CHAPTER 4 **FEED YOUR MIND** 67

The Thinking Mind 67
Choosing Your Thoughts 69
Growing the Garden of Your Mind 69
Giving the Mind Bread 70
Programming for a Positive Day 71
Other Mind-Growing Activities 72
Self-Nurturing Thoughts 74
"Flushing" the Mind 76

Poem: "The Courage to Be Myself" 81
Journaling Pages: Mind Messages 83

CHAPTER 5 **ENRICH YOUR SPIRIT** 103

The Importance of Slowing Down 103
The Dilemma of the Past and the Future 104
"Be Here Now" 107
Sensory Awareness 108
An Exercise in Noticing 109
Reconnecting With Nature 112
Enjoying Solitude 113
Seeking the Source 116

Poem: "Let the Pendulum Swing" 119
Journaling Pages: Spirit Messages 121

CHAPTER 6 **PUTTING BODY, MIND AND SPIRIT TOGETHER FOR BALANCE** 141

CHAPTER 7 **YOUR INNER LIGHT WILL SHINE BRIGHTLY AGAIN** 149

EPILOGUE **THE JOURNEY HOME** 153

A SPECIAL MESSAGE TO WOMEN HEALING FROM BREAST CANCER 157

BIBLIOGRAPHY AND RECOMMENDED READING 161

ACKNOWLEDGMENTS 165

ABOUT THE ARTIST 167

ABOUT THE AUTHOR 169

BEGINNING THE JOURNEY

It has been said that women are the caretakers and nurturers of the world. In a unique phenomena found around the world, not limited by geography, culture or religious standards, women are the ones who are seemingly responsible for the well-being of others - their partners, children, elderly parents, co-workers, friends, communities. Any woman today knows this. She may also know that women, in general, do not hold the most powerful and influential positions spotlighted by the media as those which enable our states and nations to fully function. But in her heart of hearts, she knows that it is the feminine spirit which rules supreme. It is women and their innate sense of nurturing and peace-making which hold it all together. It is women who give birth, tirelessly raise children, who are the primary caregivers to new generations, who create warm and loving households, who ensure that traditions, celebrations and holidays continue to be honored, who educate the young, nurse the sick, volunteer, give guidance and counsel. Despite this enormous load of responsibility, she moves into the workforce to carry her share of the financial burden as well. It is a big load to carry.

"But wait!", I can hear you say. . ."men's roles are changing, and more and more men are taking on the traditional female role of child-rearing, caretaking and housework." Yes, this is true in some households, but not the majority. National statistics bear this out and tell us we have a long way to go. The male and female experience are two distinctly different life experiences in the 21st century.

As women of the 21st century, we have very full plates. More and more women are caught up in the "Superwoman" trap - she is a woman who believes she can be it all, have it all, do it all, or if she doesn't yet have it, push herself until she does. Life will then appear perfect.

On the other hand, we know better. We are consciously aware that if we fall into the Superwoman trap, there will be a price to pay. We know we are supposed to stop rushing around, because it certainly can't be healthy to run at such a frenetic pace for very long. But, we are caught up in, unable to change, slow or stop the craziness of our lives. Many of us find ourselves plunked down into a seat on the roller coaster of life. Our days are a blur with people, places and events whizzing by us, and stress builds daily with no end in sight. Around and around we go.

Why are we doing this to ourselves? Why can't we just step back and say, "No, I will not get on the roller coaster today !," and take steps to break free of the Superwoman trap, to slow or change our lives? I believe that this is a very difficult, but not impossible thing for women to do today. Why? Because for countless generations, all the way back to the first caves and communities, tribes and towns, women were born nurturers. It is in our genetic make-up to nurture and bring out the best in others. In putting others first, we ensure the survival and success of the next generation and, thus, the perpetuation of society in general. Even if you are a woman on your own, without partner or children, you may know this to be true. Looking closely, you might find that much of your time is spent nurturing and meeting the needs of friends, relatives, co-workers, neighbors and the like. It is important to us that everyone around us be full, happy and satisfied (and if they are not, it must be a reflection back on us that we haven't done enough or done it right). Does this scenario sound familiar?

Barbara DeAngelis writes in her book, *Real Moments*:

> Women are the nurturers and givers of the world. We are genetically and psychologically programmed to take care of everyone. We can tune in to another person's needs before she or he can. If someone sneezes, we offer them a tissue. If someone is angry, we offer them a smile. We want to do whatever it takes to make everyone happy. We are pleasers. We love to love.

And we do. . . we love to love others to their best selves.

As nurturers, we are caught in a Catch 22 situation. We truly want to give of ourselves to others. We love to encourage and support others. It brings us great rewards and a sense of fulfillment to see others grow and blossom. We truly love to serve and find joy in doing so.

Sometimes, in this uniquely female experience of nurturing others, we begin to neglect our own needs and desires. In service of others, we give to everyone else of our bounty and find that at the end of our busy days, there is not much left at the table of life for us. We are overwhelmed, emotionally drained and exhausted.

Do you find that you over-stress, take on too much responsibility, say "yes" too often, don't rest, eat inappropriately, don't exercise, neglect your own personal friendships and, in general, have no time for yourself?

If you recognize yourself being described in these last few paragraphs, you are what I would call a "nurturer" and, if you are like many women today, you may not be taking very good care of yourself right now.

When we give so much of ourselves and our time to others, in our rush to do it all for everyone, we often lose ourselves in the process. How do you know if you have lost yourself? You probably know, but here are some helpful clues: You may have had the experience of being unheard or unseen; you may feel invisible; you may feel you have become a non-person; you may feel lost, empty or dead inside - not to mention angry, resentful or depressed; you may feel your life is out of control. You are not alone. Millions of women all over the planet feel this way. I understand how you feel, because this has been my journey, too. This is what women do. In the name of serving others, very often we sacrifice our best selves. Yet, if you search underneath the facade of Superwoman, there is a woman who has had enough, who is exhausted from trying to meet the needs of everyone, who knows she cannot continue to do so for very much longer (but is afraid that she will have to, at the expense of her own health and well-being).

If you are like me, you might be one of those women who pushed too hard for too long and had what I call a "hit the wall" experience. This could be the diagnosis of a serious health condition or cancer, a breakdown, a severe depression, alcoholism or drug addiction. Or maybe the universe gifted you a big wake-up call in the form of a tragic loss - a job, a loved one, a divorce, a home, bodily functions or valued body part.

It is at these times when we are forced to stop, not just slow the pace of our lives, and re-assess how we are living. For me, beginning in 1985, I began to suffer from symptoms of severe stress. The stress seemed to take one form or another, jumping from one part of my body to another. At one time it took the form of an intestinal disorder that caused great pain, allowing me not to eat and to look like a walking skeleton. At other times, it was insomnia or exhaustion, hives or lower back pain, migraines, bladder infections, hair loss, TMJ, PMS. . . You get the idea, I'm sure. You name it and I had it. Because I was an intelligent and well-read woman, I could plainly see that the pace of my life was causing me some serious health problems (and, interestingly enough, I was a stay-at-home mom at this point in my life, with a three-year-old and a five-year-old). I would address the stress symptom, relax a bit, slow down a little and everything would appear to be fine - for a while, anyway, maybe as long as a year. Then a stressful incident would send me into a nose dive and the cycle would begin again. What would it take to get me to realize that I couldn't continue to function the way I was? Why was it so hard to break the cycle of what I now know to be self-denial of my own needs?

If you are like me, you probably mask your symptoms very well because we don't want anyone to know we can't handle this life we have created. On the outside, you and yours, your home and life look great. But underneath, deep inside where no one else can see, is the pain and the nagging feeling that something is really wrong, and no answers to fix it.

During my most stressful years, from 1985 to 1993, no one really knew what I was experiencing internally - this feeling of having too much to do all the time, having to be so many things to so many people. I was SO TIRED. But because, I had to "put on a happy face" and "keep a stiff upper lip" as the sayings go, my internal processes were suffering. You see, it didn't make any sense - I was one of the lucky ones. I had a great family, generous husband, three wonderful children, a lovely home, satisfying life work. On the surface, I had it all. But beneath the facade, I felt tremendous disappointment, sadness, often a nagging emptiness. How could I be feeling this way, when I had such a "happy" life?

At age 40, I had what you might call an awakening. I had enrolled in several personal growth workshops and had attended a particularly moving seminar entitled *Real Magic* by Dr. Wayne Dyer, who is now my mentor. I began to experience a series of events that led me to the realization that I had somehow become disconnected. I had become so caught up in the busy-ness of life, the "doing" of life, that I was not "living" life, if you will. In typical female fashion, in doing so much for everyone, in trying to create this wonderful life for everyone, I had lost myself along the way. I had ceased to be a "human being" as Adair Lara describes in her book, *Slowing Down in a Speeded Up World*. Instead, I had become a "human doing".

Where would the nurturing come from that I so desperately needed to feel whole again - the nurturing I would so readily offer up to anyone who was feeling like I did? In searching the faces of the people around me, I knew they didn't have a clue how to make me whole again. They didn't know what I needed to heal. They couldn't put my life in order for me or help me climb off the roller coaster I had put myself on. I would have to learn to provide my own self-nurturing. I would have to love myself into an ecstatic being.

Today, my life is different. I feel that I have given birth to a new me - one who shines brilliantly inside and out. My life change involved slowing down in a fast-paced world, taking time, establishing priorities, asking for help, saying "no" to some things and "yes" to others. It meant learning to attend to my own needs instead of hoping others would know what I needed. Today, it means finding the balance between work, family and personal needs. It means learning to show and give love to myself as much as I give love to others. It means engaging in a daily program of self-care. It means finding me all over again. It means coming home to myself.

I have written this book for all of you who are struggling with the same issues I am, while searching for the balance and meaning in our lives. My belief is that until we, as women, find balance deep within ourselves, the rest of our lives will be seriously out of balance. It begins with ourselves and that means taking the time to work in our own private spaces. We need to learn to nurture ourselves, to give ourselves opportunities to grow as well as to rest and to feel good about it in the process. I am finding in my journey to come home to myself, that I need to "work" in three main areas to achieve this balance. We all need to:

- Nurture Our Body
- Feed Our Mind
- Enrich Our Spirit

and when we do, "our inner light will shine brightly again".

In this book, I will share the strategies and life-balancing techniques I have learned and continue to use today. On the motivational journaling pages I have included, I will share with you the quotes and philosophies which have helped me the most on my journey. I hope they will provide you with guidance and comfort on your journey as well. I have provided plenty of space for you to write your responses, to express your feelings, to let your thoughts soar or to record your own process.

In your journey home to yourself, you will have ups and downs, good and bad days, as in starting any new regimen. Keep in mind that this process of becoming self-aware, of finding what you need to thrive and be joyous, can be a long one. Such profound change does not happen overnight. Keep in mind also that the voyage of discovery we are all on, the journey to wholeness, is a life process. It may take a lifetime to learn our needed lessons. Be patient with yourself. Be gentle with yourself. Love yourself. Remember, you are not alone. We are all on this journey together.

The road may be long and arduous, dip and bend, twist and turn, detour with sorrow and rise with joys, but with eyes straight ahead and feet firmly planted on the ground, we will get there together. We are coming home - home to ourselves.

CHAPTER 1

LEARNING TO SELF-NURTURE: BEGINNING A PROGRAM OF SELF-CARE

Filling Our Own Wells

Learning to self-nurture is not an easy task for many of us. In traditional societies throughout the world, it is believed that the more we give to others, the more we serve, the greater our rewards will be. The rewards, interestingly enough, are believed to be received later in life, or even in the next life. Women are often told, "Your time will come later," or "You will find your reward in Heaven." No one disputes that service to others is important. In fact, I do believe that our purpose here on Earth is to do just that - to serve - but not at the expense of ourselves and our physical, emotional or spiritual well-being. Serving out of a sense of duty, which can harbor anger and resentment, or serving from a place of depletion does no one any good. Even Mother Teresa, who was the epitome of goodness and service to others, states in her book, *A Simple Path*, that following the precepts of Saint Augustine is preferable. She quotes him as saying, "Fill yourselves first and then only will you be able to give to others."

In communities of old, there was a centrally located well, where all townsfolk came to draw water, replenish themselves and gain sustenance for the day of work ahead. In my seminars for women, I enjoy using the metaphor that women are very much like wells. Everyone comes to us to "drink". They receive sustenance, support and encouragement. If we have given birth, we may literally have them drink from our bodies in the form of nursing. We are supposed to know what everyone needs from us and provide it unconditionally, lovingly. The well must always be full for anyone who may stop by for a drink.

If we are not careful to personally replenish our own wells, we can dry up. The need for giving doesn't end. People still come to the well to drink, but there may be no water for them anymore. The well is depleted or at a low level, at best. Our loved ones, friends, co-workers, neighbors cannot drink from an empty well. We have two choices of how to begin to fill our own wells so we can continue to nurture others without self-neglect.

First, we can let others know what we need for self-nourishment and replenishment. Do your loved ones truly know what you need to be able to relax? Do they know what things and activities cause your spirit to soar? Have you told them, or do you hope they will know by osmosis? A better question might be, do you know what you personally need right now to feel less stress and more meaning in your life? Many women I have worked with are not sure anymore. They have been on the fast track for so long, they have forgotten what it will take and how it will feel to be relaxed and peaceful. Or the dreams once held for a deeper, more meaningful existence loom too far out on the horizon to be reached for anymore. It is important that you take the time to do some self-assessing to find out what you want or need and then create the opportunity to communicate your wants and needs with those around you.

The second choice is to immediately take steps to fill your own well and begin self-nurturing activities with or without the support of others. This is sometimes difficult because we keep hoping and waiting for others to see our signs of burnout or stress and take the steps to nurture us, as we would do for them. Unless you have a very open, supportive and communicative network of people around you, it is probably not going to happen. You will need to seize the day and begin to do for yourself. If you are feeling angry or resentful that others can't nurture you the way you want to be nurtured, my advice is to let it go. It will serve no positive purpose to stew over it. Harness all that wonderful energy and put it to good use on YOU! Begin today to take the necessary steps to treat yourself like the majestic creature you are!

Assessing Your Current Ability to Nurture Yourself

It may be useful at this time to find out where you are in your ability to nurture yourself. How easy or how difficult is it for you? How much self-nurturing are you currently doing?

Take a few minutes to complete the survey I have created for you. Listed below are 50 activities which could be classified as self-nurturing. In the space provided, put an "X" next to each activity you have engaged in within the last month.

______ 1. Took a leisurely walk
______ 2. Read a book for new knowledge
______ 3. Rode a bike or rollerbladed
______ 4. Took a hot, leisurely bath
______ 5. Did nothing
______ 6. Had a massage
______ 7. Engaged in your favorite sport
______ 8. Stayed in bed all day

______ 9. Watched a sunrise/sunset
______ 10. Listened to music
______ 11. Jumped in a puddle
______ 12. Read a book for escape
______ 13. Laid in the sun to feel its warmth
______ 14. Had a facial, pedicure or manicure
______ 15. Planted flowers or trees
______ 16. Took reflective, meditative time
______ 17. Built a sand castle
______ 18. Went to a movie
______ 19. Took a brisk walk for exercise
______ 20. Had lunch/dinner with a special friend
______ 21. Made a snow/sand angel with your body
______ 22. Danced
______ 23. Sat and gazed into a fire
______ 24. Went away for a weekend
______ 25. Smelled flowers
______ 26. Baked bread or cookies
______ 27. Had a picnic
______ 28. Hugged yourself
______ 29. Played on a playground
______ 30. Complimented yourself
______ 31. Watched a thunderstorm
______ 32. Daydreamed
______ 33. Listened to the birds singing
______ 34. Laughed long and outrageously loud
______ 35. Went for a swim
______ 36. Took a class or learned a new hobby
______ 37. Roasted marshmallows
______ 38. Celebrated your own birthday
______ 39. Stood in the rain and felt it on your face
______ 40. Pampered your body with scented oils, lotions
______ 41. Went to a library or museum
______ 42. Sat and cried
______ 43. Went on a nature hike
______ 44. Had a tea party
______ 45. Fed the seagulls/birds
______ 46. Bought yourself a gift
______ 47. Climbed a tree
______ 48. Stayed in your p.j.'s all day

______ 49. Gathered seashells along the shore

______ 50. Ate something truly decadent without guilt

Now, go back through your responses and count how many "X's" you have.

Take a few moments to reflect. How do you feel about your total? What do you think your answers reveal about your capacity to take time just for yourself? For some women, taking a survey like this is very eye-opening. They may feel they do plenty for themselves, but now realize they could be doing much more.

I hesitate to give scores for a survey like this, but let me share with you what I have found after administering this in my seminars for the past several years.

Many of the women in my seminars were doing less than 50% of these self-nurturing activities. Most women score themselves at 15 to 25 (or 30% to 50%). This is not to say that we are failing at self-care. Let's just say there is plenty of room for improvement !

The real purpose of this survey is to give you some tangible ideas of how you can begin to embark on a program of self-care with simple and fun activities, like taking a leisurely walk, indulging in a warm bubble bath or going to a movie with a friend. Simple things - yes. But self-nurturing pleasures are always the first to go and to be cut from our busy schedule or put on the back burner to attend to something else or someone who needs our attention.

I would suggest taking this survey again a few months down the road, after you have been on this new path of self-nurturance that I am about to share with you. Many of my workshop attendees are amazed at their survey results 6 months later and are proud to share their stories of progress with others. You can also use this survey to come up with new ideas of activities you can try - maybe things you have never done before - like receive a massage or facial. You may want to create a "Wish List" for yourself of all the wonderful things you would like to do for yourself. Keep reading and I will share with you the techniques I have learned to use to do good things for myself. YOU CAN TOO!

Self-Aware Versus Selfish

One of the biggest roadblocks to beginning a program of self-care is the feeling experienced by many women of being selfish. Why is it that when we do good things for ourselves, we automatically assume that

1). Someone else will be deprived or neglected if we do for ourself, or 2). Doing something for ourself is self-centered and shallow?

I believe women have been tremendously dis-served by this notion - that we can take time, spend money or indulge in self-pampering only:

- If we have done all our other work
- If no one else needs us at the moment
- If we have extra money to spend.

What all these statements seem to shout at us is that we and our personal time are not as valuable as others and their time. The roots of women's challenges with self-esteem and self-worth can be found here. Somehow we need to convince ourselves that we are worth it; we are worth time, money and personal attention. I am always reminded of this challenge by the L'Oreal commercial with Cybill Shepherd who fluffs and swings her gorgeous, newly colored, blonde hair and confidently states, "I am worth it!" If Cybill can do it - we all can do it!

What it really boils down to is a question of self-love. Self-love has gotten a really bad "rap," if you will, in 20th-century culture. If we love ourselves, we most certainly must be self-centered, egotistical and shallow. I offer you here, a new definition of self-love - because without a workable definition, we will continue to fall into the same old patterns of self-neglect.

Peter McWilliams, in his book, *Love 101*, defines self-love as, "Taking care of, with regular intervals of taking good care of, and occasional splurges of pampering." He points out that when we "love" someone else, we take good care of them. We bend over backwards to make sure they are happy, well fed and cared for. When we truly love someone, we strive to help them reach their personal best, to be their best selves.

So why do we have such difficulty showing this kind of love to ourselves? As you know, thousands of books have been written on the topic of self-esteem and self-worth. If you had asked me at any point in my life whether I had high self-esteem, I would have answered an unequivocal and resounding, "YES!" But, did I love myself enough to learn to give and show MYSELF the love I needed, just as I would do for others? Not necessarily. It seems more important to show love to others first. After reading those hundreds of self-help books, we all know we need to love ourselves, or we can't effectively love others. So . . . what's the problem?

Giving Yourself Permission

It is hard to break old patterns, to turn off the chatter that runs through our heads, not just from our previous generations, but from thousands of years before us. Remember, we spoke before of this - this sense of a need to nurture everyone, which is at our core. Core issues do not resolve themselves easily, but they can with Baby Steps - small steps taken one at a time to make little changes that are manageable. This is what I present to you here in this book. The small ways, even in as little as five minutes per day, that we can begin to break the old patterns and begin a new journey to a new us - one that is loved and feels worthy of time, money and attention.

I challenge you to give yourself permission to do all that you can and to be all you can, so you may discover your best self. When you do this, you will find over time, your personal well feels wonderfully full and, as you have blossomed, so have those around you. As you have spent time on yourself, loved, pampered and nurtured yourself, your well fills and all who come to you to drink will be better served. Let go of the guilt and give yourself permission to toss that gorgeous head of yours and say, "I am worth it!"

Giving Up Perfection

In the last few paragraphs, we spoke of the first big step one needs to take to begin a successful program of self-care - Permission, permission to be self-aware. With that issue addressed, we can move on to the second step - Giving Up Perfection. Many of us have struggled with the idea of personal perfection. We are bombarded with media messages to be and have it all - the gorgeous figure, the lovely well-groomed children, adoring life partner, the house beautiful, the charmed professional life. Rarely do we have even one of these, but in our quest for self-worth, we continue to strive to achieve, if only for appearances, these elusive standards of perfection. This struggle for perfectionism takes it toll on us - physically, emotionally, mentally and spiritually.

In the interest of self-nurturing, we realize that our idealistic, perfectionistic life goals will have to go. In her wisdom, the late Erma Bombeck said, "A woman can have and do it all, but not at the same time." Indeed, something will have to give if you are going to find "me" time, relaxation and self-nurturing opportunities. We cannot do it all, all at once - nor is it healthy to try. I agree with author Ann Wilson Schaef who writes, "Perfection is self-abuse of the highest order."

Giving up perfection is difficult, to say the least. I found it helpfully inspiring to read in *Simple Abundance*, by Sarah Ban Breathnach, that she struggled with perfection and now lives by the motto, "Progress - not Perfection." I like that quote . . . I can live with progress! If I can continue on my own program of self-care and take time for my own well-being daily, I guarantee you nothing in my house will be perfect. We will make progress, but it doesn't have to be perfect. It is comforting to know that someone else's family laundry gets done, folded, but not put away - that the kids pulling their school clothes each morning from a laundry basket will not traumatize them for life!

It may be harder on other people than on you, to give up perfection. In my household, it forced other people to take on more responsibility (which is good, but often resisted). As a nurturer, it was always easier to say, "I'll do it." Now, when the laundry is piled too high, beyond his comfort zone, my husband throws in a load of wash and folds it, too. Like most nurturers, I thought that if I didn't do it personally, it wouldn't get done right, that only I knew the right and best way. Come to find out, he actually does laundry better than I do!

Do not be surprised to find resistance as your standards change. No one in any household or workplace likes change. Here is an example from my personal archives: When I began to take more time for myself, not everyone was happy about it. I decided that each evening after 9:30 P.M. or so, when the children were tucked into bed, that I would begin my "me" time. With the dishes done, I headed to the master bathroom for a nice soak and a good book. Yes, there were plenty more chores that could be done - the ever present laundry to be folded, drawers to be cleaned, papers to be organized. But I chose to let those go until tomorrow and take some well-deserved relaxation time. As I climbed into the deliciously steamy tub, Gothic novel in hand, my husband walked in and caustically commented, "It must be nice." Yes, it was. You see, unlike many women who would have folded and given in to the pressure to keep at the daily grind with exhaustion setting in, I had reached my limit and I chose not to give in. I fought for my precious "me" time. I had resistance, because as I changed my priorities and my routine, my loved ones would be forced to change, too.

Today, this evening routine remains a staple of my self-care program. It took approximately 3 weeks of persistence to let my family know I meant business - that I needed, and would take, evening time for myself and I would not be dissuaded or side-tracked from doing so.

Remember, learning to live with progress, not perfection, takes time, patience and persistence. Be gentle with yourself.

Prioritizing for Personal Time

Establishing Priorities is the third step to self-care. At some point, we all have to sit down and figure out what is really important on a day-to-day basis. Daily self-nurturing time is crucial. If you are going to create time for you, then you will probably have to re-structure your day, give up certain standards and activities and go for it! Take a few minutes and write down on a piece of paper what you feel to be the most important things you need to do each day. Then, ask yourself the following questions for each item:

1. Does this have to be done each day?
2. What will happen if I don't get this task done?
3. Can I get someone else to do this for me?
4. If I delete this activity, even for just a few days, what will happen?

Only you know what daily activities are crucial and cannot be cut back, delegated or even eliminated. What can you let go to create more time for yourself? (In Chapter 6, we will do a time management exercise to help you with this.) What can you say, "No" to and, "Yes" to, for yourself?

Again, a personal example: When two of my three children were in elementary school, I was working outside the home and volunteering heavily at their school. In fact, I was so committed to the idea of school volunteerism, I was willing to pay for child care for my toddler in order to do so. When I began to feel overwhelmed and stretched too thin, I knew something had to go. I had always been room mother (usually for two classrooms at the same time), sat on numerous committees and chaired one major school event each year. In 1993, I announced I was done volunteering. I stepped down from all committees and took on no new responsibilities. I remember feeling like a huge weight was lifted off my shoulders. Of course, no one liked that I said, "No" each time I was asked to serve again. In fact, as time went on and everyone knew that I was dead serious about no new responsibilities, that I was taking one year off for me, the cold shoulder treatment set in. I could feel a huge shift occur and found that the people previously surrounding me moved away. Why? Because I refused to fill the role of inexhaustible nurturer and servant anymore. I am sure, to them, I seemed selfish and unconcerned about school affairs. Not so. I had learned where my limits and boundaries were and tuned in to my own depletion levels. What I had to do at the time for my well-being was to give up volunteering.

In your own program of self-nurturing, there will come a time when you will have to learn to say, "No." Others may not like it, but as we have discussed, it is central to your primary care needs. It is okay to say, "No."

It is also okay to say, "Yes." Confused? In this respect, I mean there also comes a time when you may have to ask for help from others and admit you cannot do it all. This is especially prevalent if your health is at risk. When we receive a personal or professional diagnosis that we need a life change to slow down or stop, that we will need to give up or relinquish responsibilities, it is very difficult for a nurturer to do so. Learn to receive and appreciate the gift of support and encouragement and don't be embarrassed.

I recall a time when a chronic bladder infection had kept me housebound for many weeks. Very little got accomplished at my house, due to my pain and frequency issues. On one day that was especially bad, I was lying in bed nearly unable to move or care for my children, when the wife of my husband's boss called to say that she heard that I was ill and could use some help. I was mortified that she would come into my sorely neglected home and see an unkempt me languishing in bed. I shuddered to know what she would think. She said she was coming to take my youngest child for the day to give me a break. I agreed, and after I hung up the phone, I sobbed with relief. When she arrived, out of necessity I was in the bathroom, so I held onto my dignity and relinquished my child to her. What a wonderful gift she gave me.

It is very difficult to accept help sometimes. When we are overwhelmed and in danger of falling apart, we need to learn to seek out those individuals who will understand our plight. Admit to imperfection and accept assistance. Often it is only with such assistance that we can begin the road to healing and wholeness.

Setting personal priorities may seem difficult at first, because it forces us to restructure our lives. Change is not easy. By prioritizing, you will find out who you really are and what it is you want. You will learn what is important and what can be let go. You will arrive at a new definition of YOU. Establishing priorities and acting on them takes courage. Be strong, my friend, and make the necessary choices to move forward on your journey.

Being Passionate about "Me" Time

Getting time alone when you are a busy woman is no easy matter. With the demands of children or elderly parents, it is even more so. Developing a passion for "Me" Time is the fourth step to self-care.

I recently ran into a woman whom I had not seen in over a year. I hardly recognized her. She had lost a tremendous amount of weight and looked haggard and gaunt. I gave her a hug and asked her how she was. She poured out a heart-wrenching story of how she was care-giving her elderly mother (who was now also living with her), how her husband had suffered a severe stroke and was not the same man as before. They had owned a business together, but were now filing for bankruptcy because neither of them could run the business anymore. She was exhausted with caretaking. Her main complaint, though, was that she had no privacy and no time for herself at all. Looking into her eyes, I saw incredible pain and longing - longing for a respite, some quiet time and solitude with no demands. We discussed some options for her, but her outlook was bleak at best. Here was a vibrant professional woman who was in great danger of not only losing her mother and husband, but of also losing herself in the care-giving process.

It is up to each of us to find the right amount of time we need to rest and re-fuel. This means private, alone time. With our alone time, we can do many things. We can seek solitude and peacefulness. We can seek out adventure and excitement. We can get caught up on much needed sleep. We can tackle a creative pursuit or project that speaks to our heart. It doesn't matter what you do with your alone time - just that you take it with a passion. When we give so many pieces of ourselves away to others, we must learn to schedule in precious time for us. If you are not used to taking time for yourself, except to complete the daily necessities, even beginning with 10 to 20 minutes per day may seem like a lot. If you have a more flexible schedule, you may find that with prioritizing, you can free-up a few hours. It truly is a matter of priority.

At a recent seminar, I administered the self-nurturing, self-assessment survey. Many of the women in the audience were current or retired business women. The oldest woman in the group, I guessed her to be 80 or so, interestingly enough had the lowest score. She had marked two items out of 50. Even in her retirement with a full day of positive choices awaiting her, she took no self-nurturing time. She "worked" all day and did things for others.

Another middle-aged business woman in a seminar took the survey and came to a startling realization. She had taken a week off of work to stay home, rest and relax instead of travel on a vacation. The first five minutes into her week off, she was on the phone with friends and colleagues, arranging activities. She said, "I realized how I don't even know how to sit and relax anymore. I couldn't cope with sitting there, listening to the quiet." Needless to say, at the end of her week off, she admitted she was still exhausted.

Then there is the story of a young mother in her 20's who convinced her family she needed to get away by herself for a weekend to retain her rapidly dwindling sanity. She registered for a weekend retreat at a women's center along the beautiful shores of Lake Michigan. The weekend program was filled with wonderful opportunities to grow, self-nurture, relax and have fun. There was a great speaker, a massage therapist, a winery tour, dinner out, a video night - you get the picture. This young mom checked in on Friday night, came out for meals at the appropriate time and headed back to her room. On Sunday morning, she emerged from her room, bags packed and began to profusely apologize for her lack of participation. She said, amidst tears, that it was the best weekend of her life. You see, what she did all weekend was sleep.

My point is that if we can begin to schedule amounts of "me" time each day and build on that private time, we need not reach such levels of depletion. The key is learning to schedule it in. If we wait until we have fewer commitments and more time for us, we are fooling ourselves.

We schedule in mammograms and dental visits. Isn't our emotional and spiritual health as important as these - important enough to be scheduled in? In Chapter 6 we will do an analysis of your day and find the precious time you need for your own self-nurturing. Until then, take 20 minutes per day to do exactly what you want to do - something that will replenish you and enable you to carry on until tomorrow.

For those of you with care-giving challenges, it will be up to you to find a support or respite system of other people who can help you do this. If you have small children, maybe it is finding child care so you can have a private day off for R&R. Maybe a shared care system or co-op can be found through a local agency or church. For elderly care-giving, the same applies. Check local organizations, churches or private nursing agencies for assistance. Barter with a friend or neighbor for shared care. Trade a night out with a partner or spouse and do the same for them. Get creative. It is totally up to you to be passionate about your private time. As I stated before, no one else knows what you need unless you tell them and then it will be up to you to make sure that it happens on a regular basis.

~ ~

In closing this chapter, I am reminded of a poem by Shel Silverstein from his poetry anthology, *A Light in the Attic*.

"This Bridge"

This bridge will only take you half way there,
To those mysterious lands you long to see:
Through gypsy camps and swirling Arab fares
And moonlit woods where unicorns run free.
So come and walk awhile with me and share
The twisting trails and wondrous worlds I have known.
But this bridge will only take you half way there -
The last few steps you will have to take alone.

I hope you will find the beginning steps I have outlined in this chapter helpful as you launch your program of self-care. I feel they are a bridge - a bridge to wholeness.

CHAPTER 2

GETTING STARTED

Creating Balance in Life

In my strategies to create a sense of balance in my life, I have found that three main areas needed daily attention. I did not always have the time and energy to give adequate attention to each. Therefore, I found myself seriously off balance, and when you are off balance, so is everyone around you. Remember the old saying, "When Mama ain't happy, ain't nobody happy."

The foundation on which my personal program of self-care rests is the universal principle of balancing body, mind and spirit. In my own life, it seemed balance was never attained. I would be caring for one part of myself and not another. For example, if I was getting a good amount of rest and relaxation, I wasn't exercising - thus, weight gain. Or, if I was engaging in mind-fulfilling activities, like reading or researching, I found myself on mental overload, not taking adequate time for quiet and reflection. I often felt like an uncoordinated flamingo, standing on one leg, ready to tip over at the slightest wind gust.

When I began to find shorter times daily for 1). Body, 2). Mind and 3). Spirit-based activities, I noticed that I felt much less stressed, more peaceful and, in general, complete. I created my own personal care program based on daily scheduling for each one of the three cornerstones. *I found it very comforting to know I had taken care of my whole self each day.* This is the format I have taught other women for over 4 years and many tell me it has transformed their life. In the following chapters we will learn together to do the following:

- Nurture the Body
- Feed the Mind
- Enrich the Spirit

What do I mean by each of these? In "Nurturing Your Body," you will learn how and why to find time for movement or exercise and the importance of healthy eating. We will explore together pampering principles and techniques to relax and send messages of self-love to your body.

In "Feeding Your Mind," we will explore how the mind functions to create a new self-image every day and how the messages we send to our subconscious can be maximized for personal growth. We will learn how to fill our minds with "good stuff" and how to "flush" them as well to provide inner calm.

In "Enriching Your Spirit," we will look at taking the time to re-connect with yourself and nature, your earthly purpose, your spirituality. We will discuss ways to truly slow the pace of our lives, learning to live life to its fullest by connecting with the present moment.

For each of these three areas of focus, we will also learn time management strategies so that you can incorporate them into your daily routine easily and effortlessly. You will also learn to reward yourself for all of your hard work and dedication to creating your best self.

It is important to follow the steps in order, as I outline them here in the book. We begin with body and move to spirit. The time management strategies come at the end. Throughout the text we will continue to emphasize and illustrate how each of these three parts need to be attended to for life balance.

Life presents interesting surprises for us, as we journey on this path to wholeness. I have used and taught the precepts here for four years in my home state of Michigan, and occasionally elsewhere in the United States. Recently I have come across more and more individuals who use the same principles but with a different format. That provides wonderful validation that we certainly must be on the right track and that women's self-care is of utmost importance.

I have been reading a book called *Conversations With God*, by Neale Donald Walsch, as have millions of other seekers worldwide. In it, "God" states a profound concept that we have already discussed here. I would like to share it with you. He talks with the author and proclaims that putting yourself first does not mean what we term "selfish." It means being self-aware. He goes on to state, "We are three-part beings - Body, Mind and Spirit. Those of us who see ourselves as that, is very small. When you live as a three-part being, you come at last into balance with yourself."

I found this very gratifying to read and feel more motivated than ever to get out this important message of self-nurturing to all who will listen. I believe this three-part model works in helping to create a sense of wholeness for those of us who are struggling with these issues. I do not want to give you the impression that I have mastered these techniques outlined in this book. I am a human woman, imperfect at best, making progress at the least and dealing with one day at a time. I continue to have my own personal healing challenges; yet I know this system works. When I find myself getting off track during high stress times or when the pace of my life has speeded up as it is wont to do, I can go back to my "routine" and almost immediately feel a sense of calm come into my hectic life. If I could shut the world out and stay exclusively focused on my self-care regimen, all would be well. But we all live in the real world and every day has its new challenges. I hope the system presented here will bring you a sense of security and control over your life as it has mine.

Journaling to Wholeness

You will notice if you have looked ahead through this book that there are empty journaling pages. I feel compelled to include these as a major stepping stone on the path to achieving balance and seeking wholeness. Writing through pain and illness can be a profound healing tool. Why writing? I almost prefer this to the word "journaling" because it does not sound so time-consuming or based on long-term commitment. Writing is giving voice to our silent thoughts, feelings, desires, joys, sorrows, hopes and dreams. An empty journal page can lend an ear to the unsaid within each of us.

As little girls, we are often told to be quiet, to whisper, to walk softly, to be lady-like, not make a fuss. Sociological studies and the use of video footage today document this phenomenon and show us that we are still sending much of the same programming to young girls. It is more acceptable for boys to be vocal and show anger through physical expression than for girls to do so. These messages run deep within our conditioning, making it difficult for many women to transcend their childhood programming that quiet and unobtrusive behavior is the most desirable form of behavior.

That is why I believe it is so important for women to "sing their truth." If we cannot sing it out at the top of our lungs, we can certainly write it fast and furiously on paper. The important thing is to express it in some way and in so doing, to understand our inner process. *What cannot be expressed cannot be healed.* We must give form to our thoughts and feelings.

In *Healing Mind: Healthy Woman*, Alice Domar, Ph.D., explains the importance of letting it all out through journaling. She writes:

> When you stick with the process, writing becomes a journey that naturally wends its way from deep feeling, to insight, to

> acceptance. It is like following a yellow brick road from the source of trouble, a traumatic event or situation, to a healing resolution rooted in awareness. Forgiveness of self and, in some cases, forgiveness of others . . . The writing process as one way to process difficult emotions, can also help us to make transforming life passages."

Dr. Domar uses writing exercises as part of an intensive program she leads at New England Deaconess Hospital for women with stress and stress-related illnesses. She also uses writing as a healing tool with women who have breast and gynecological cancers, PMS, infertility and menopausal challenges.

When I first began to write, those initial blank pages loomed large, so big and empty. What was I supposed to say? At first I would write down only phrases, feeling that this was enough. It reminded me of one of those old-fashioned pressure cookers, where you lifted the lid just a little and enough steam came out to give momentary release, so the pot wouldn't explode. To take the whole lid off would have been too much to handle, and it would have created an enormous mess besides. Instead, I felt comfortable taking what I call Baby Steps. Write a little, reflect a little. I didn't even write regularly - only here and there when Spirit moved me. But I always felt great relief afterwards. A little tip of the lid was all I needed to get me through.

I tell you this to give you encouragement to begin using the following pages to write down some initial thoughts about yourself and your process. Don't put pressure on yourself to write a certain amount, length or time. Write as you are moved to do so. You may find, as I did, that after a while, the process becomes cathartic and desirable. I looked forward to my writing time, for I knew it would provide much needed release. As time went on, I could literally feel healing energy pour into me, as my words flowed onto paper.

You may find that your struggle may begin with words of self-chastisement or criticism. In *The Unimaginable Life*, a new book by song-writer Kenny Loggins and his wife Julia, Kenny recalls his first journal entry of 1984. He wrote then, "Why can't I write? What's all the resistance? It's as if I'm afraid I won't have anything to say, or I might discover this is all an exercise in futility, an excuse for schizophrenia, conversations with myself and not very good ones at that." Kenny goes on to explain how, as he continued to journal, he was "amazed at both the clarity I had kept locked up inside of me and my willingness to put it on paper."

One technique you might want to try is to write letters. They are often called unsent letters (although you may opt to send them, as well) and they are a prime opportunity to talk to someone openly and honestly about your feelings and emotions. You can write a letter to a partner, to God, to a friend, a child. A letter to yourself, as you are now, can be revealing - or conversing with your inner child can be helpful as well. If you are faced with a healing challenge, a letter to your illness or an affected body part can provide insight also. Jan Phillips in her book, *Marry Your Muse*, describes letters to the muse, her creative self, which the muse lovingly answered.

The national bestseller, *Conversations with God*, attests to the profound information revealed by using another technique - that of asking questions. Simply write the question down at the top of the page and wait for an answer to begin to write itself out. Who is doing the answering? Good question. You may be surprised to find that you have the capacity to answer your own questions, that the answers and guidance you are seeking are all within. Some call this the Higher Self, others may call it intuition, others consider it to be Divine Guidance. Listen to and heed the revealed messages. *Your own words have the power to heal you.*

Writing, to me, is like therapy (and a lot cheaper!). After a day away of writing, as in this book, for example, I come home feeling purged, cleansed. Those around me notice the difference. I feel lighter and happier because for a brief period of time I have let my creativity soar, my thoughts run free and unrestricted. My emotions spill forth onto paper like a long dormant volcano spews its fiery liquid, causing all life in its path to be forever changed.

Writing, for me, is a profound experience. In a world that moves too quickly to listen, writing allows me to speak my truth. As ink flows, the paper accepts my words and absorbs them. I have been heard. No other ears are necessary when paper is present. Naomi Wolf writes, "Only one thing is more frightening than speaking your truth - and that is not speaking."

There is no right or wrong way to journal. Some people find it helpful to write upon arising in the morning, recording the first thing that pops into their head. Others find their best journaling is done at night, releasing the day's frustrations and stresses onto the paper.

The key to journaling success is to write what you really feel. This can be a frightening prospect, especially if you feel you may not be ready to deal with the emotions that may rise to the surface as you write. Be comforted, however, in the knowledge that once emotions are set free, the journaling process can be a tonic to the soul. In the words of Simone Weil, "If we go down into ourselves, we find that we possess exactly what we desire."

Your writing experience can be whatever you make it. For women with chronic illness or pain, studies show that journaling in conjunction with a self-care program can alter stress levels and improve longevity. It can also improve relationships. One woman recounts in *Healing Mind: Healthy Woman*, that writing enabled her to open up to others by allowing her to unload and "leave her baggage at home." Kenny Loggins shares in his book, *The Unimaginable Life*, (a book based on and full of journal entries) that his journal became a "safe harbor." It allowed him to arrive at a place of wholeness where he was then able to give and receive a new type of love he had never experienced before - the love he shared with his soon-to-be wife, Julia.

Dr. Domar writes in her book, "Whether women are lonely, angry, struggling in their careers and relationships or beset by medical conditions, they can use the writing process to get on with their lives with confidence. It is a remarkably effective and illuminating approach to mental, emotional and physical well-being."

The writing pages I have included in this book have motivational quotes on them. These are not just quotes randomly picked from volumes of such phrases. These are the quotes I learned to live by. They were, and remain today, transformational for me. They help keep me on my path of self-nurturing and enable me to maintain focus. They keep me self-aware. I hope that they serve you as well.

Every person's journaling experience can, and should, be different. It is your inner voice speaking to you and everyone's inner voice is uniquely different, just like each of us.

~ ~

As I close this chapter, I am again reminded of song lyrics that attest to the power of journaling - this time from Kenny Loggins' "Will of the Wind" which he wrote in 1989 as part of his creative writing process:

The voices in the wind
Will take you home again.
The journey home has just begun
My friend.

CHAPTER 3

NURTURE YOUR BODY

Our body is a precious gift. We are given one body to live in during our existence here on Earth, to live life to its fullest, to be aware, energized and capable. We all need to take good care of our body. This needs to be done in three ways: To eat healthfully for longevity and to be disease-free; To exercise for body strength and agility; To nurture and pamper our body, giving it rest and rejuvenation. What are you doing on a daily basis to be good to your body, so that it will serve you well?

~ ~

This chapter, "Nurture Your Body", is not about creating the perfect body. It is about capturing perfect health so the body in which we live can remain strong, useful and energetic for our lifetime.

This chapter is not about body care for the purpose of looking or being a certain way. Women have been tremendously dis-served in our culture by societal expectations as we are bombarded with images of thinness, youth and beauty. These pressures to look and be a certain way, or to be a specific size, cause women incredible emotional and spiritual pain - pain that we are not good enough; we are not trying hard enough; we are not disciplined enough. Most certainly, if we were, we would be thin and beautifully attractive. There must be something wrong with us.

The issue of body size and weight causes an emotional firestorm in women. It is up to each of us to begin the journey to leave societal expectations behind and seek a new relationship with our body. We can learn to take the first steps to come to a loving relationship with our physical form - one where we listen to, and heed, our body's inner messages. We can learn to be good to our body and give it what it needs for optimum performance and for relaxation. We can learn to de-stress ourselves and gently pamper our body, sending it messages of love and support. We can create a strong, vibrant body through healthy lifestyle changes that are amazingly easy, once we make the commitment to do so.

It is not my intent to instruct women on nutritional and dietary needs or exercise regimens to make lifestyle changes. That has all been done before with thousands of books, magazines and television shows. Deep in our psyches we all know what we should and should not eat and how we should exercise for optimal living. We have heard it from so many sources, for so long, we are sick to death of hearing it. My purpose here is to motivate you to take the first few Baby Steps to take control of your life, through better living habits.

We are just beginning to understand the effects that nutrition and exercise have on our mental and emotional well-being. Because we are a body/mind/spirit organism, when the body suffers or feels distress, the other two parts of our self do also. Emerging studies show that if proper nutrition and exercise is not upheld, mental and emotional processes can be profoundly affected. In order to keep the balance we have talked about, it is crucial that we pay as much attention to our body as to the other aspects of our self.

Robert Gerzon writes in *Finding Serenity in the Age of Anxiety*:

> Many clients I have worked with have experienced substantial, often amazing, psychological benefits from such simple lifestyle changes as getting more sleep (fatigue alone will induce anxiety symptoms), eating a more natural, balanced diet (some people are actually allergic to the very foods they crave), and exercising regularly (without exercise, tension and stress accumulate in the musculature and create biological anxiety).

I speak here from personal experience. The body connection has probably been my weakest link in the three-part chain of total wellness. It was always the part that I had the least time for. It seemed as if there were other parts of me that needed more immediate attention. My body could be put on the back burner for one more day, until I got caught up with the rest of my life. I would promise myself that I would eat healthier tomorrow or that I would exercise this weekend, when I had more time. Instead, if I did have free time, I would much prefer to read a good book, visit with a friend or take a well-deserved nap. To shop for and prepare healthful food took more time than I had. Exercise took even more time and energy. I didn't have either. Not until my health took a serious turn, did I feel compelled to make eating and exercise lifestyle changes. The same may ring true for you.

When I made the connection between health and longevity, the desire to make changes occurred. Instead, I found myself asking, "How badly do you want to live? Do you want to live long enough to enjoy your children as adults? Do you want to live long enough to play with your grandchildren?" Not until I had a "hit the wall" experience with my health, was I willing to make the necessary changes to do so. That may be the case for you as well. I had to get passionate with my own life to take the steps necessary to re-learn how to eat and exercise properly. My new motto became, "Ya Gotta Wanna!" Nobody could make me exercise or eat the proper food. I had to learn to do it for myself, from my own sense of deservedness, from a place of self-love. That is an especially hard task when you find yourself looking in the mirror, not loving what you see.

Before beginning a new relationship with your body, you may have to spend some time getting to know it, learning how you feel about it and why you have allowed it to receive the inattention it has in the past. Some of you reading this have come to the realization that your body can be a sacred vessel and you are treating it like one. I commend you. Keep up the good work! For those of you who struggle with these issues as I do, let's take the first few steps together, a few Baby Steps at a time.

Eating Healthfully for Longevity

One of the most important things we can do is to honestly assess our current eating patterns and how they impact our total health. Food, for most people, is an emotional issue. Why? Because food symbolizes many things to many people. It may be a source of comfort or a reward. It may provide missed nurturance. It may give a sense of fullness, when one feels empty. I am not a therapist, but I was able to analyze my own eating patterns - what I ate, when I ate it and what the surrounding circumstances were. I think deep inside we all know what it is we feel about food and our relationship to it. However, if you are unclear or need assistance, I would recommend a good therapist or psychologist, or the current books on the subject.

My personal favorite is the book, *Constant Craving: What Your Food Cravings Mean and How to Overcome Them*, by Doreen Virtue, Ph.D. In it, Dr. Virtue explains the emotional connection we have with food and goes so far as to catalogue hundreds of foods and the emotional ties (cravings) we have with them. It is a profound piece of work.

By looking at the foods we are currently eating, we may uncover the emotional ties that bind us to these foods. For example, Dr. Virtue connects such specifics as cravings for bread or pasta as a need for comfort and calming; high fat foods with a need to fill a feeling of emptiness, and so on. She reaches the conclusion that, "Your entire body, including your appetite, reflects the level of peace of mind in your life."

For me, the shift came when I realized that food consumption was indeed related to a feeling of emptiness inside of me. I began to notice patterns in my daily life. When I was feeling particularly good about my life, when all was flowing smoothly, I felt energetic, enthusiastic and healthy. I didn't seem to require much food. I was so busy doing what I loved to do, my mind wasn't on food. When I did eat, I unconsciously chose healthy, mostly vegetarian, low-fat foods. I felt like getting outside, enjoying nature and exercising. I also noticed the reverse to be true. In a nose-dive toward stress, once again I would self-sabotage. I would be too busy to eat "real meals" and would stuff whatever was available into my mouth to stop the hunger pangs. I would not exercise because I didn't feel up to it, sending messages of low energy to my body.

It took many years of misusing my body to realize that as Dr. Virtue describes, "fat is a spiritual issue" (so is thin, if you are a binge eater or anorexic). The body/mind/spirit connection is so strong that our spiritual progress or lack of it can, indeed, take its toll on our physical body.

It may take therapeutic work on your behalf to break any unhealthy dietary or eating challenges you have. Our relationship with food can be as deep seated as infancy, connected with adolescence or based in relationship issues. It is a complex issue, one that may take a long time to unravel, but it is a must if eating disorders or unhealthy consumption are a barrier to your total health. Take the time to analyze your personal relationship with food.

With a mental shift to engage in healthier eating habits, we now move to *"how?"* We all have been on one diet or another and most of us have come to the realization that diets don't work. In fact, we now know they may cause more harm than good. It is not a diet that will bring us new-found energy and a healthier body. It is a change in eating habits that will do so. This involves a sensible, modest approach to eating.

I do not want to take a lot of time here to spell this out, as there is an abundance of resources available to us on this topic. I do recommend one in particular that I have referred to before: Dr. Alice Domar's, *Healing Mind, Healthy Woman*. In the chapter entitled "Mindful Eating, Modest Exercise" she outlines very simplistically how women can begin to make small changes to improve their dietary lifestyles. I particularly like her chart entitled "Eating Transitions" where she lists items you may be currently eating and how to gently substitute different items of improved quality and lower fat content. This chapter is full of profound, easy to use advice to begin the journey to "healthy woman."

When we have the passion and have made the commitment to move toward perfect health, we are sending loving, supportive messages to our body. By filling our body with nutritious, healthful food, we are literally sending it messages that say, "I love and honor you. I want to be with you for a long time. I love this vessel in which my Spirit lives." This is an ultimate act of self-nurturing. Our body listens to these subconscious messages and responds immediately. You will experience a feeling of centeredness, that you are now back in control and that your body is coming back into balance. It begins to thank you by sending you energy and a new-found peace of mind. As we continue to send "I love you" messages to our body by eating for longevity, our body whispers back, *"I love you, too."*

Movement for Longevity

If you are like me, the word "exercise" may conjure up a plethora of negative associations like - hard work, sweaty, time consuming, not fun, boring. I have always struggled with exercise for many reasons:

- I didn't have the time
- It was too difficult to get started and maintain a program
- It made my muscles hurt too much in the beginning
- I had no energy to exercise
- The routine became boring and I lost interest

I have always known I needed to exercise, if I wanted to live healthfully and to a ripe old age, but doing it was another thing altogether. It seems that there are more excuses and rationalizations to not exercise than any other activity one can engage in.

An article in *Newsweek* magazine shouted the headline "Exhausted!" The byline read, "We are fried by work, frazzled by the lack of time. Technology hasn't made our lives better, just busier. No wonder one-quarter of us say we're exhausted. We need to chill out before we hit the breaking point." Health and wellness professionals tell us we need to de-stress ourselves and our lives to prevent reaching this breaking point, and one of the key ways to do it is through exercise. The Catch-22 is, how can we possibly find the time and motivation to exercise when we are too exhausted to do so? Do we sit on the couch and wait for the energy to come?

Unfortunately, our bodies don't work that way. If we sit and wait for energy to appear, we will sit forever. Movement is what brings energy into our lives. It will be up to you to force yourself the first few times to *get up and move*. But once you do, within a few days you will notice a significant shift in your energy. Doubtful? Try this experiment. Take a few moments and put on a piece of your favorite music. Listening to the rhythms, whether they be slow or fast, begin to move to the music. You don't have to dance, just begin to move parts of your body to the beat. Almost simultaneously you will feel energy begin to course through your veins. You will feel like you want to keep going, as if the music can carry you and your body away, time and space forgotten. You see, movement creates energy. We need to get up and move and then we will feel the benefits of new-found energy.

The key is to begin a simple, uncomplicated exercise regimen. Truthfully, I call mine a "movement program" because it eliminates all those pre-existing negative associations I have with exercise. Physicians interviewed in *Newsweek* (March, 1995) go on to describe how moderately intense physical activity in as little as 30 minutes per day can begin to give most people significant health benefits. Doing this in increments can make it easier to fit into your day. You can do three 10 minute walks per day or two 10 minute walks plus 10 minutes of stair climbing. You also get credit for housework and yard work. If everyone in the United States were active only 30 minutes per day, 400,000 lives would be saved each year from cardiovascular disease. Cardiovascular disease today is the #1 killer of women.

This may sound like a lot of time to you, especially when you look at your daily schedule and see no 30-minute time slots looming large as life. You may have to begin with as little as 5 to 10 minutes per day, so that you can move toward 30 minutes three to four times per week. Later, we will look at your daily schedule and help you find some time slots for personal movement. This is the first small step to establishing life balance. Make a commitment to engage in movement activity so your heart will pump not only healthy, oxygenated blood, but beat with passion for your newly discovered healthy self.

The second key to movement for longevity is to find a form of movement that you truly love and that makes you feel good. It is not necessary to suffer through the physical ordeal of aches and pains to benefit from movement. The most enjoyable times in my life are when I am walking briskly amidst the beauty of nature, soaking in the sights and sounds around me. My heart is getting a wonderful workout, but I am not suffering or struggling. A successful movement program will be one you love to do and look forward to doing regularly.

Studies today show that fast walking is probably the easiest and best form of movement we can engage in. We all can find places to walk, whether they be indoors or out. It is finding the ardent desire to do it daily that is sometimes difficult to hang on to.

I have often shifted from one form of exercise to another, depending on time, money, circumstances, child care and general health. I also switched exercise forms when I found myself getting bored. That is the third key to the success of your personalized movement program. Move on to a new medium if you find yourself getting bored.

Ask yourself before choosing a new form of exercise the following questions: Do I want companionship or do I want to do this new movement form alone? Will I feel comfortable, not self-conscious, in this element? Will it be affordable? Will I be willing to take the time to go to a place (gym, pool) to exercise or should I stay at home and do it?

I have tried just about every form of exercise possible. I found I was most successful in programs where I was not feeling self-conscious or uncoordinated, ones in which I had a companion to go with for motivation.

Today, as I write this, I am regularly engaged in yoga practice two to three times per week. On my non-yoga days, I fast walk. My walks last for no more than 30 minutes. A yoga class is a bigger time commitment - one hour plus travel back and forth - but it is worth it. Later in this chapter we will explore the total health benefits of yoga.

The third key to movement success is being gentle with yourself. Remember that all lasting progress is slow. Your body will begin to respond with time and attention. For yoga, it took almost 3 weeks for me to begin to feel the tremendous benefits. For walking, usually within 10 days to 2 weeks positive results will be shown. It is not necessary to go fast and hard in the beginning of any exercise regimen. Remember that you have made a lifestyle commitment and this takes time to truly implement. You will be doing this from now on, so it is all right to choose the turtle's pace rather than the hare's. We all know who won that race - and that is precisely the point. This is not a race to health. This newly established path to total health is part of our life's journey, one in which commitment and persistence are of primary importance. Paramahansa Yogananda, the founder of the international spiritual movement, Self-Realization Fellowship writes: "Establish a controlled attitude wherein you can work with peace, without losing your balance."

Movement for Spiritual Practice

Many of us who are exercise-resistant struggle to find a movement form which is fun, non-threatening and inexpensive but yet effective for optimum health.

A recent episode of television watching found me mesmerized by an infomercial featuring weight-loss guru, Richard Simmons. His program featured "Sweatin' to the Oldies" among other forms of dance to promote personal wellness. His stage and audience participants joyously moved to the music. They obviously were having a great time. They weren't in pain or struggling. In fact they seemed oblivious to the fact that they were sweating, burning calories and toning their bodies. All they were doing was dancing!

Many of us love to dance or move to music. Some of us are great at it. Others of us resist because somewhere along the line, we internalized messages that we couldn't do it right, we were uncoordinated or had two left feet. Maybe our self-esteem was not strong enough to withstand a critical eye watching us. We worried that we would make a fool of ourselves out there on the dance floor, while others looked on.

Can you put a stop to that negative self-talk and allow yourself to recapture the feeling in childhood of running and being free? Do you recall being able to whirl and twirl to your heart's desire until dizziness set in and you laughingly tumbled to the ground. . .the sky moving in circles, around and around over your head?

As children, we used to move with confidence and purpose to our inner rhythms. As adults, for whatever reason, we may have lost touch with that sense of spontaneity of movement.

Today there appears to be a renewed interest in dance as a movement/exercise form available not to just gifted dancers, but to everyone. Movement artist, Gabrielle Roth, has done much in recent years to educate us in the art of "movement as spiritual practice." She encourages us to use dance, not just as a form of exercise, but as a "self-healing ritual, a passionate offering to the Divine." When we harness the energies of our body, we can also utilize the other two parts we have spoken of before in our balanced approach to life - that of mind and spirit. What an optimum opportunity dance can be to connect body with mind and spirit.

In her new book, *Sweat Your Prayers - Movement as Spiritual Practice*, Gabrielle Roth writes:

> To sweat is to pray, to make an offering of your innermost self. Sweat is holy water, prayer beads, pearls of liquid that release your past - a baptism by fire. It is an ancient and universal form of self-healing, whether done in the gym, the sauna or the sweat lodge.

> I do it on the dance floor. The more you dance, the more you sweat. The more you sweat, the more you pray. The more you pray, the closer you come to ecstasy. Mine is a dancing path."

I offer this to you as an option for your movement program. For those of you who are exercise-resistant, "spiritual dance" may be a way for you to find a deeper connection with your body. As ancient and tribal traditions have shown us, a deep body connection can bring about profound mental and spiritual awareness, one that leads to a total picture of optimum health on many different levels. Our physical body, mental processes and spirit are deeply connected at a root level. As Roth describes, "The soul cannot breathe, exist or move, disconnected from the body." When we move our body, indeed we also move our soul to a new place on its journey.

Fine Tuning With Yoga

As a junior in college, I discovered the benefits of Hatha Yoga. Back then, when I lived so much of my life in my body (as young people are wont to do), it provided an excellent form of exercise. Through a college physical education class, I found that yoga kept my body fit and trim. It served me and my body well, and kept me strong and supple.

Today, in my 40's, I have rediscovered the tremendous benefits of yoga for total health along with many men and women nationwide. My yoga practice of today lends itself in a different way to a body that has not been treated too well in its 40+ years on the planet. I look around my yoga class and see many individuals, like me, who feel their years in their body and hope to hang on to flexibility and strength. Through a gentle and caring teacher, I have learned to get slowly back in touch with my body, to listen to and honor it.

Yoga practice offers much to busy women who may feel stress and mental overload. Through gentle stretches and movement (postures called 'asanas') it provides a reawakening of the body's sense of self and inner wisdom. It stretches the spine, muscles and ligaments. It enables the body to reduce its own stress symptoms and relieve muscular tension. It helps the mind to slow down and find focus on simple movements of body and breath. It also provides relaxation.

Yoga, for me, has been one of the most challenging things I have ever done, but also one of the most gratifying. The exercises are not difficult, with a good instructor. The difficulty often lies in the fact that many of us are running daily at such a frenetic pace, we feel our exercise regimen must be that way also. The challenge is to learn to slow down and get back in touch with our body. This involves quiet, slow, rhythmically gentle movement. Sometimes our mind screams "Faster!," but the breathing exercises, the foundation of yoga practice, force us to concentrate on the here and now. With a subtle stretch or twist, with an intake or outflow of breath, the mind becomes calm and focused and the body responds with subtly increased flexibility and strength.

I found that yoga practice was the perfect antidote for my racing mind and heart. It enabled me for even 2 hours per week (I started a gentle regimen of yoga twice weekly) to let go of the busy-ness of life and concentrate totally on myself. The breathing exercises provided me with a chance to focus on absolutely nothing but the importance of breathing in and breathing out. The relaxation exercises carried my mind to places of peace and respite. I would leave renewed and replenished.

I strongly suggest yoga practice, either with a personal instructor and class or by using one of the many excellent videos on the market for in-home use. Alice Domar, Ph.D. writes, "Yoga can be a godsend to women with racing minds." It was for me, and I highly recommend it to you.

I also would like to make you aware that a new form of yoga is emerging which is more aerobic in nature, if that is what you seek, called "Power Yoga." It incorporates more intense cardiovascular work for optimum health. Just as there are dozens of exercise programs and instructors available, so are there myriads of types and styles of yoga. Seek one out that fits the profile you are looking for. Seek the regimen that best fits the body/mind/spirit connection you are searching for. Yoga, like sacred dance, can move you into a new spiritual space. Once again, combining body, mind and spirit into one discipline can have profound and lasting effects - effects you will feel on all levels of your being.

Breathing For Life

Part of our daily self-nurturing regimen should also include breathing exercises. Most of us are not even aware of our breathing in and breathing out process and why it is so important for health.

Cathy, my dear friend and massage therapist, taught me about the importance of breath. Whenever in the craziness of my day I might see her, she would gently lay her hand on the small of my back and say, "Breathe." My response would be, "I am" and she persistently continued, saying again, "Breathe." She would force me to stop in my tracks to let the gentle healing power of breath make itself known to me.

Those of us rushing to and fro in our day-to-day existence don't think about breathing. It is a natural phenomenon that occurs without us consciously thinking about it - we just do it. Most of us breathe shallowly from our chest in short gaspy breaths. In doing so, tension seems to build and sit right in the middle of our chest or up through our head, neck and shoulders. I am sure you have all felt the difference in yourself when you become aware of such tension and the immediate result that occurs when you take a deep breath. Breathing in deeply and exhaling deeply releases the tension within. This, of course, works not just for bodily tension, but mental and emotional tension as well. When we become conscious enough to deepen our breathing down past our chest into our abdomen, we feel the difference in our state of body/mind.

Interestingly, Dr. Alice Domar in *Healing Mind, Healthy Woman*, notes that women especially don't take a single healthy breath. Why? Because we are too busy holding our stomachs in! In trying to look thinner, and denying the natural shape of our body, we sacrifice the power of breath to heal us.

As we breathe deeply, our body receives specific benefits. Our blood is oxygenated, which provides new, healthy blood to flow to our brain enabling us to think more clearly. It flows to our organs to allow new cell reproduction. It flows to our muscles and ligaments, allowing them to gain strength and become more flexible. With deep abdominal breathing, our body harnesses its own innate healing energy. It also enables our mind to relax and let go of stored up negative emotional energy and thought processes. Deep breathing allows us to be quiet, to get in touch with the stillness within which can bring peace of mind. In other words, deep breathing can enhance the quality of our physical, mental and spiritual selves - all at the same time.

In yoga practice, deep abdominal breathing is central to reconnection with body, mind and spirit. Simple exercises to gently deepen breathing give immediate results. You can try this yourself by breathing in deeply through your nose. Start by filling your lungs with air and continuing breathing until the abdomen puffs out and feels full. Do this slowly, counting from 1 to 5. Hold your breath for a brief second, then exhale slowly through your mouth - slowly emptying the abdomen and lungs to another count of 5 . You may even want to give a final push of air out to totally clear your lungs. As this becomes easier with repetition, you can extend your breathing time; breathing in to the count of 10, holding briefly and exhaling to the count of 10. As breathing slows, your pulse, heart and metabolic rates slow. Focusing on counting your breath allows your thought processes to focus and slow. Deepening your breath can take you into a deeper meditative state of relaxation. There are many patterns of breathing that can be used for varying benefits. I would recommend *Conscious Breathing*, by Gay Hendricks, Ph.D., to further explore how the power of breath can enhance the quality of your life.

In seeking ways to reduce my own stress level, I found what I call *breathwork* to be invaluable. My friend Cathy, the massage therapist, uses breathwork exercises for 15 minutes with each client before she even begins a massage. In doing so, she put me in touch with how powerful my own breath was to relax and heal myself. Breathwork and yoga especially allowed me to still my racing thoughts and reduce anxiety.

Today I seek regular time daily to focus on my breath. I have incorporated it into my daily regimen of self-care. The method that works well for me is in the bathtub or shower. Combined with the nurturing warmth of water, I can count my breathing, letting out tension and bringing in peace and calm. At night, once tucked into bed, I may also do breathwork to ease into the sleep mode. Deep breathing allows me to "de-tox" and let go of mental chatter, bringing restful sleep. Another good place to practice deep breathing is in the car while you are driving. It takes no extra time at all to engage in conscious breathwork. Once these patterns are learned, you can use the power of breath anytime, anywhere, without anyone even knowing it. You may be surprised at the level of calm it brings and how people notice a difference in you. I have also taken my breathwork to a deeper level (more than just for relaxation and stress reduction), to further my personal meditation practice and to engage in greater spiritual awareness. The simplicity of conscious breathing with intent has brought me much joy and inner peace.

Thich Nhat Hanh explains in *Living Buddha, Living Christ*, that conscious breathing is the most basic Buddhist practice for creating peace. He describes a short exercise that I have found to be most helpful to me and I would like to share it with you. Take a few minutes daily to do the following. Being aware of breath, say to yourself:

> "Breathing in, I calm my body.
> Breathing out, I smile.
> Dwelling in the present moment,
> I know this is a wonderful moment."

Another exercise he suggests is:

> "Breathing in, I am aware of my heart.
> Breathing out, I smile to my heart.

I vow to eat, drink and work in ways
that preserve my health and well-being."

Here again we have the body/mind/spirit connection. As we breathe in, our heart is nourished with newly oxygenated blood, our thoughts slow and our spirit finds peace and serenity.

Nurturing ourselves with the miraculous gift of our own breath is simple and amazingly effective. It just takes the remembrance daily to do so. In the words of Thich Nhat Hanh, "Go slowly. Breathe. And smile."

Creating "Island" Time

As busy women of the new millennium, it is doubtful that we have many opportunities to get away from it all, to rest, pamper and rejuvenate our body. Many of us wistfully look through travel magazines, longing for the ideal vacation where we can be fed healthy, gourmet food, be massaged and pedicured, pampered or we would love to soak up the warmth of the sun, stroll under moonlit skies with a leisurely walk, have time to just plain *BE*. We long for extended weeks with no responsibilities, no phone calls to return, no meals to cook, no laundry to catch up on. Sometimes, when the pace of life is too much to take, we can even empathize with those women who chuck it all and run away.

Writer Anne Morrow Lindbergh, was indeed a wise woman. In the 1950's she wrote *Gift From the Sea*. In it, she discussed the importance for women to take time alone, as she was doing on a vacation by the ocean. She spent her days wandering the beach, collecting shells, learning lessons from them and writing about it. After collecting one particular shell and reflecting on it, she wrote:

> Moon Shell. Who named you? Some intuitive woman I would like to think. I shall give you another name - Island Shell. I cannot live forever on my island, but I can take you back to my desk in Connecticut. You will sit there and fasten your single eye upon me. You will make me think, with your smooth circles winding inward to the tiny core, of the island I lived on for a few weeks. You will say to me "Solitude." You will remind me that I must try to be alone for part of each year - even a week or a few days; and for a part of each day, even for an hour or a few minutes, in order to keep my core, my center, my island quality. You will remind me that unless

> I keep the island quality intact somewhere within me, I will have little to give my husband, my children, my friends or the world at large. You will remind me that woman must be still, as the axis of a wheel in the midst of her activities; that she must be the pioneer in achieving this stillness, not only for her own salvation, but for the salvation of family life, of society, perhaps even of our civilization.

Is it possible for you to do as Anne suggests - take alone time at least once each year for a week or a few days? This would be a special time to meet only your own needs, to do exactly what you want to do, to enjoy solitude - a time for you to give your body well-deserved rest and the pampering it deserves. Is it feasible for you to do this? Do you have a support system to help you do so? Would you really want to spend time all alone with just yourself as your own best company?

If days alone are not an option, then smaller increments of time each day may be desirable. Can you find time in your day just for you - to be alone, to rest or pamper your body so it continues to serve you well?

I have found that small increments of "Me Time" keep me feeling much more balanced and stress-free in my daily life. I describe it to my family as "private" time. It is time I use to nurture myself however I see fit. It can be at home or away from home. It may be as short as 5 minutes or as long as many hours. I try to include self-nurturing activities, like the ones listed on the Self-Nurturing Self Assessment Survey in Chapter 1. I may try to include self-pampering rituals such as those I describe in the next section. Whatever they may be, they are activities that need to be done alone so your body can continue to receive the time, attention and messages of self-love it needs to hear.

Some women I know choose to keep a personal Sabbath. With professional or family demands taking so much of our precious time, many of us no longer have a weekend Sabbath day. Weekends are for playing catch-up. A cartoon I recently saw portrayed this: A little boy approached his mother and asked her, "Mom, what are we doing this weekend?" His mother responded, arms overflowing with laundry, "What's a weekend?" A personal Sabbath is one day per week - any day of the week you choose - dedicated only to what you want to do. It is your own personal day for rest, relaxation, enrichment, fun, self-pampering or nurturing.

Those of us with physical healing challenges, like cancer, or chronic conditions, like fibromyalgia or chronic fatigue syndrome, need to give our body this much needed time for self-indulgence. Remember, our body is a "thinking" body; we are a "body-mind," as Deepak Chopra states in his many books. When we send messages to our body that we are worth time and attention, it responds in kind and begins to say, "I love you" back to us. This may come in the form of increased energy levels and maybe, if we are fortunate, improved health.

Following the advice of Anne Morrow Lindbergh would serve us well. Let us seek out our own solitude time, so we may hold on to and maintain our sense of center, our "island quality." In so doing, we can continue to give and serve others when called upon. In giving to ourselves, we give to others.

Self-Nourishing Rituals

As we create pockets of "island time," we will want to include regular, predictable activities which nourish our body and spirit, giving us respite from mental overload. I call these "self-nourishing rituals." The word "ritual" can be defined as a ceremonial act or series of such acts. Self-nourishing rituals embody the sweet, small things we can do regularly for ourselves. They slow our mind, enabling us to focus on the here and now, engage our senses and allow us to luxuriate in "just for me" time.

The key to a ritual such as this is that the steps or key ingredients be performed in exactly the same pattern each time. This provides the comfort of "sameness" - the relaxing feeling of what to expect while knowing that nothing else needs to be done other than to sit back and enjoy. As a result, we gain the pure pleasure of enjoying the moment for exactly what it is, a moment in time when we can truly *BE*.

For me, my nightly bathing ritual is paramount to my daily existence. The simple ritual I have created surrounding my bathtub is something I look forward to every day. It is my reward at the end of any day, busy or not. I also re-create this ritual as I need to at various times of the day if stress sets in or if I am not feeling well. I set the stage with my reading glasses, the special book of the moment, my favorite bath or shower gel (and if at evening, sometimes a glass of wine) and, of course, peace and quiet. This bath ritual may take 15 minutes or as long as an hour - time is not important. I drain and refill the tub so the water stays at the perfect temperature. I forget the world that lies outside the bathroom door and slide into a world of comfort.

For me, the bath is very therapeutic. It meets my physical, emotional and spiritual needs for nourishment. Your self-nourishing ritual can involve anything that enables you to let go and surrender to the moment. This can take many forms including: aromatherapy indulgence, comfort foods or clothes, a date with the sun, a massage, a commune with nature, etc.

Jennifer Louden, author of *The Woman's Comfort Book: A Self-Nurturing Guide for Restoring Balance in Your Life*, has literally created an encyclopedia of over 200 recipes and rituals for relaxation, comfort and self-care. She even provides a quick reference guide to use when you are feeling a certain way, such as: Feeling overwhelmed? Try "using your nurturing voice" or "creating a comfort network" or "hiding under the covers" - only three choices from dozens she gives you and teaches you how to use. This book is a phenomenal resource for those of us in need of self-care.

In creating the perfect self-nourishing ritual for yourself, identify what it is that actually gives you comfort. What feeling do you want to have as you are having the experience and how do you want to feel when it is over? What materials or props will you need? What time frame are you working with? How will you have to set the stage, so to speak? Be creative and devise a wonderful way to give yourself permission to enjoy YOU, where your body purrs in contentment and your mind luxuriates in pleasant surroundings.

Again, remember whatever your body nourishing activity might be, do it regularly with the same intent, preparation, tools and setting. Done on a regular basis, this predictable pattern of ritual can move our body and mind toward a state of wholeness. We begin to remember how it feels to be peaceful, unified and free. As memory stirs, we feel propelled to re-create this again and again until it becomes a normal part of our day, each and every day.

Creating Healing Space

Do you have a place in your home that is yours and yours alone? According to author Virginia Woolf, every woman needs two things: her own money and her own room. As part of your self-care regimen, there are tremendous benefits in carving out a place of your own. I am sure we would all love our own rooms, filled to the brim with the colors, smells and things we truly love. That would be the ideal situation - create a space you can go when the voice of solitude or self-indulgence calls you. Have it designed and set up so that the moment you enter, peaceful thoughts greet you. It would be a perfect place, not unlike a little Eden, where your senses are surrounded by beauty.

However, in real life, most of us share spaces with partners, children, grand-children or friends. Our spaces are full of other people's stuff - which given a choice, we personally wouldn't have there at all. We have to be realistic here in carving out a niche for ourselves amidst the clutter of busy households.

In creating a healing space, our goal is to select and use a space that can be as small as a desk top or as large as an entire room. This space enables us, like our self nourishing rituals to leave stress and strain behind and move into a place of comfort.

I have met many women who have carved out their own niche in a household that bustles with activity. My friend, Ellie, moved into a new house and selected a small extra bedroom for herself that she dubbed her "angel room." She painted it a favorite color, filled it with her favorite books and music, endearing photos, motivational prints and fragrant candles. She goes there to renew focus or to get away from it all.

Without the luxury of an entire room, we can claim a corner or section of a room as "ours." I don't have the luxury of a room of my own, so recently I created a cozy corner for myself. I bought a lovely oversized wicker chair with a tapestry cushion and a reading lamp. It sits in a corner by a built-in bookshelf. I removed all the books and started from scratch. I replaced them with my personal favorites - some I have read, some I have not - but whose titles and covers give me sustenance. On top of the bookshelf are scented candles, a pottery blessing bowl of a woman, a carved stone in her lap that says, "Strength" and a miniature watercolor of a woman celebrating a celestial sky. I removed the knick-knack shelf that had been there for 7 years and hung a motivational print I found in a gallery. A basket full of my favorite magazines sits by the chair. It is my corner and I love to sit or read there. Surrounded by favorite things, relaxation comes more quickly. My body feels safe; I feel "at home."

A dresser or desktop can serve the same purpose. A small nightstand by your bed, carefully arranged with your favorite things, is another option. Even a space as small as that sends messages of self-importance and worth to you and those around you. You have claimed your own space, or territory, which further validates the need for personal time and space. By creating healing space, we devise another way to communicate with our body that it is special, deserving of beauty and comfort.

Loving Touch

We have discussed many ways thus far to send positive messages to our body - messages that say, "You are worthy, you are loved, you are enough." One of the most profound but underrated methods is the use of loving touch. It logically follows that if our body is a "thinking body," then it will respond to stimuli that awaken our senses. What more obvious way to awaken remembrance of being well and whole is there than lovingly touching our body?

Often when we feel less than whole, or are suffering physically, we feel betrayed by our body. We believe it hasn't served us well and we harbor anger toward it. As a result, many of us get out of touch with our body. We hide and cover our body and don't allow it the privilege of being touched. We may recoil from another's touch because we are embarrassed at our body's current condition. We may also recoil from our own touch and avoid touching ourself. By allowing ourself to be touched, we begin to change the messages our body is receiving. Loving touch sends messages of worth and self-esteem and helps restore the body's memory of when it was vital and fully alive.

The touch can be your own or that of another. I recommend incorporating both into your self-care routine in the form of massage.

Self-massage is a profoundly personal way to send positive messages of love and comfort to your body. In the shower or bathtub, using scented lotions or oils, we can lovingly nurture our body, easing tension and pain. As we slowly massage our skin, receptors open, activating nerve endings which then send messages along the spinal column to the brain. Touch is the most basic form of communication we can send to ourself.

In *The Power of Touch*, Phyllis K. Davis writes, "We now know that feelings of love generate physical events. Touching communicates love, consciously or unconsciously and can trigger metabolic and chemical changes in the body that help in healing. Tactile stimulation and emotions may control endorphins - natural body hormones that control pain and our sense of well being." When we touch slowly, lovingly and gently, these messages of value and nurturance unconsciously manifest themselves. Our vulnerable psyche picks them up and with repeated use begins to accept them. We begin to remember how special we are.

Partner massage is wonderful, too, but in keeping with our overall purpose of the book, our goal here is to establish patterns where we do not necessarily rely on another's care for us to thrive. If you are fortunate enough to have a partner to engage in shared massage, I encourage you to do so. It will benefit you both.

Much more is being learned today about the benefits of massage therapy. Phyllis Davis writes,

> Massage relaxes the body, thus reducing stress, not only at the time the massage is taking place, but by way of teaching the body how relaxation feels. It is a method of re-training the body to respond, not with tension, but with relaxation. Massage also increases circulation, thus releasing toxins from the body. It increases sensation and energy and promotes a general sense of well being if done properly.

I am always amazed when I gather the results of the Self-Nurturing Assessment Survey (see Chapter 1) at my workshops, to discover how few women have ever had a massage. For some women it is an issue of finances. Massage can be expensive and we may feel that our money could be spent in a more practical or useful fashion. Many of us have never had a massage because of our insecurity about our less than perfect body. We cannot imagine that a total stranger could touch and accept our body as it is. We are sure they will notice all of our lumps, bumps and bulges and think us unsightly. However, the reverse is true. Licensed massage therapists do what they do because they desire health and wellness for all their clients, no matter what shape or form their body takes.

Massage at the hands of a trained therapist can facilitate the healing process. When someone else cares enough about our well being to spend an hour or more kneading and working our muscles, helping us to relax and achieve a peaceful state of mind, we again process unconscious messages of worth and acceptance. Massage can re-ignite a sense of care and concern about your body and motivate you to take even better care of it.

If it is difficult for you to justify the expense of massage, put a request for a massage gift certificate on your birthday or holiday wish list, and let someone else gift it to you. The gift of massage is one of the greatest gifts of self-nurturance you can give yourself.

~ ~

Commit today to spend at least 15 to 30 minutes each day, nourishing your body. Challenge it with healthy movement for longevity. Make a vow to learn new ways to eat healthfully and develop eating patterns which will improve the quality of your life. Spend 15 minutes or more each day with a self-pampering ritual or practice.

Sue Patton Thoele writes in *The Woman's Book of Spirit*, "When the body is too tired, malnourished, overworked, stressed-out or lacks enough exercise, it begins to falter, system by system. . .we have ravaged our temple. We need to realize the sanctity of our body and make it a priority to tend to it responsibly and respectfully."

Love yourself enough to give your body temple what it needs. By committing to perfect health, you show the love to yourself that forms the basis of a lifetime commitment to self-nurturing.

Doorways

"Never" said the little girl
"Shall I walk up to the door
Behind the door lies darkness
Will fear be evermore?"

"Never" said the little girl
"Shall I knock upon the door
Behind the door lies sadness
Will pain be evermore?"

"Never" said the little girl
"Shall I open up the door
Behind the door lies changes
Will change be evermore?"

"Maybe" said the little girl
"Shall I look inside the door
Behind the door lies brightness
Will sunshine be in store?"

"Gently" said the little girl
"Shall I step right through the door
Into the Light I venture
Self love forevermore."

Cathy Caldwell
(reprinted with permission)

It's the fire in my eyes and the flash of my teeth, the swing of my waist,
and the joy in my feet, I'm a woman phenomenally.
Phenomenal Woman, that's me.
Maya Angelou

To love oneself is the beginning of a life-long romance.
Oscar Wilde

Wherever you live is your temple if you treat it like one.
The Buddha

It's fine to want to look attractive,
but it feels best when you do what seems natural, not phoney,
and when you start, not from a position of self-hate and insecurity,
but from one of self-love and acceptance.
Karen Katafiasz

Taking joy in living is a woman's best cosmetic.
Rosalind Russell

Self love is the only weight loss aid that really works in the long run.
Jenny Craig

Just remember, a nice hot bath can solve almost any problem.
Author Unknown

Beauty means vitality, imagination, energy—
personality traits that have more to do with an individual's character
than his or her age or some idealized arrangement of physical features.
Anita Roddick

Experience self-acceptance deep within,
in every part of your body, mind and spirit.
Be at ease; you have a right to your place in the universe.
Karen Katafiasz

I will remember to be gentle with myself
with all the tenderness, respect and love
that I would give my only child.
Joan Borysenko

Go slowly, breathe and smile.
Thich Nhat Hanh

If you want to give birth to yourself,
you are going to have to dig deep down
into that body of yours and let your soul howl.
Gabrielle Roth

Sometimes it is easy to be generous outwards, to give and give and give, and yet remain ungenerous to yourself. You lose the balance of your soul if you are a generous giver but a mean receiver.

John O'Donohue

Lured by love, the crocus kept spring's promise.
Lured by love, I too will flower...
K. Sherman

When the world outside seems difficult to take,
and the stress in your life becomes overwhelming,
look inside for your strength.
Julia Mitchell Marra

Coming into wholeness as a woman
isn't so much about discovering who you are,
but about taking back the parts of yourself you gave away.
Barbara DeAngelis, Ph.D.

I celebrate myself, and sing myself.
Walt Whitman

I am enough.
Nancy Scheibe

What remains now is the deepest healing of all, the healing of love.
Deepak Chopra

The universe is so wonderfully constructed that all paths lead home.
Robert Gerzon

CHAPTER 4

FEED YOUR MIND

Your mind is also a precious gift. You have choices every day of what to fill your mind with. If you fill your mind with positive thoughts and experiences, your personality becomes positive, as does your behavior. The opposite is also true. Let us feed our mind daily with enlightening literature, stimulating conversation and meaningful activity. Your mind also needs time daily to rest, to empty, to revel in quiet. As your mind expands, your whole world grows and changes. What are you doing each day to grow your mind and create a positive life for yourself?

The Thinking Mind

Many of us go through our life mundanely performing tasks day after day. We are literally on auto-pilot. People, places and things move in and out of our daily experience. We don't give much conscious thought to what we experience, yet we tend to believe these happenstance events have little bearing on such things as our beliefs, attitudes and feelings. They are just there - in our life for one moment, out the next - the person who sits next to you on the bus. . .the song you heard playing on the elevator this morning. . .the angry encounter you overheard between two neighbors. These are minor events at best which have little or no significance in our life - or do they?

When we begin to develop a greater understanding of how our mind works, we realize that even small mundane events impact our thinking and feeling processes and, subsequently, our behavior.

I recall the first time I became aware of this process years ago. I was working for a national direct sales company which specialized in self-esteem-based music for children. A psychologist, Dr. Michael Popkin, was a featured speaker at our national convention. Dr. Popkin presented what he called "the Think-Feel-Do Cycle of Behavior". This was totally foreign to me, even with my educator's background and 10 years of classroom teaching experience. He proceeded to explain how it is that we become who we are. I had always held to the theory of child development that part of our personality makeup was hereditary and part was learned from our nurturative environment. Dr. Popkin believed that outside stimuli or "data" helped create who we are to a much greater degree than we are aware. He went on to explain how even small things, seemingly insignificant things like sounds, sights or smells, can have a profound impact on us. They affect our thoughts, feelings and actions. Of course, he was speaking primarily of the formation of a child's personality and behaviors, but upon further consideration, I knew he was also talking about me as an adult.

I began to think about what daily stimuli in my environment were affecting me, positively or negatively, to create the *ME* I am each day. I became acutely conscious of my daily routine, of the people, places and things that came into my life. I also became super-sensitive, if you will, to the sensory stimuli around me - heightening my five senses to be more aware of what was going on around me.

Upon further reading and study over the next few months, I began to carefully monitor the input (experiences) that I allowed into my daily routine. Why? Because I realized Dr. Popkin's theory did make a great deal of sense. I realized that we do have a choice each day of what to fill our mind with. The input that we allow into our mind on a daily basis forms our thoughts. The cycle does not stop here. Our thoughts then become our feelings. Every feeling we have, whether it be joy or sorrow, jealousy or generosity, starts with a thought first. The thought we think and the emotion we feel results in a behavior. Again, every action has a feeling and a thought at its origin. To summarize, *we truly are what we think about*. Input creates thoughts, which lead to feelings, which become behavior. This is the Think-Feel-Do Cycle of Behavior. This, combined with hereditary factors, is how we become who we are.

We have choices every day of what we put into our mind. We can become acutely aware and consciously choose what goes in to our mind, thus impacting our thoughts, feeling and behaviors.

This is a difficult concept for many people to grasp because we have lived so long with the notion that our thoughts just happen. We believe that feelings arrive out of nowhere and there is very little that can be done about it. Thoughts and feelings simply pop up and there is little we can do to control them.

When you come to the realization that you do have power over your own thoughts, your life will dramatically change. This is an important realization, because this means that you are primarily responsible for your own thoughts. No one can make you think or feel a certain way. Your thoughts are your own - they originate inside of you. As you create your own thoughts, you are literally creating yourself. *As you think, so shall you be*.

Choosing Your Thoughts

In the late 1800's, an Englishman named James Allen penned an essay entitled *As a Man Thinketh*, which was destined to become a landmark in the human potential movement. Today, Dorothy J. Hulst translates this classic for women. She writes, "A woman is literally what she thinks, her character being the sum of all of her thoughts."

In determining what we want our character to be, we will need to take a serious look at the input we allow to enter our daily regimen and thoughts. If we have the power to harness our thoughts, we have the power to create a new ME each day. Dorothy Hulst goes on to say,

> Mind is the Master-Power that molds and makes,
> and Woman is Mind, and evermore she takes
> the tool of Thought, and, shaping what she wills,
> brings forth a thousand joys, a thousand ills;
> She thinks in secret, and it comes to pass;
> Environment is but her looking-glass.

The process of creating a new ME begins with making conscious choices of what to feed our mind daily. I particularly like the analogy of the human mind as a magnificent computer. The input we put into our personal computer, the mind, will determine the output. What we put into our individual data bank can be carefully selected, entered and processed.

For example, given a choice, would you feed your mind with positive thoughts or negative ones? What will result from positive thoughts? Positive feelings and behavior. The same is true of negative thoughts. (In computer terms, this is called 'GIGO' - Garbage In, Garbage Out.) But if we feed our mind with positive input, thoughts and experiences, our personality and behavior toward others will be positive. In the greater picture of things, this is what we all seek . . . a positive, loving, joy-filled existence.

I call this process, "Feeding Your Mind." If we feed our body nutritious healthy food for maximum performance, shouldn't we also give our mind the same nourishment? Let us seek to discover ways to feed and give sustenance to our mind. I particularly like how speaker and author, Jim Rohn, describes this process. He says, "Give your mind bread!"

Growing the Garden of Your Mind

In my work with women over the years, I have likened this process of learning, of growing your mind, to the act of gardening. As we begin to work in our own personal garden, we carefully choose the seeds we will plant because we know that what we sow, we will reap. If we want daisies, we must sow daisy seeds. We will not get roses out of daisy seeds. We must choose, keeping mindful of long-term outcome, what goes into the soil. Next, we nurture and enrich the soil. We lovingly tend it, providing water, sunshine and nutrients. We also remove weeds which could stunt or inhibit our growth. With time and attention, our garden blooms brilliantly.

Our mind functions in the same way. When we choose what we want to reap in the future, we will plant carefully and conscientiously now.

Giving the Mind Bread

What are you filling your mind with each day? Given choices, do you:

- read a good book or choose a supermarket tabloid?
- listen to music or to sensationalistic talk radio?
- watch public television or soap operas?

Which of these activities gives your mind bread and allows it to grow? When we expose our mind to enriching, empowering activities, it can do nothing but grow.

We will need to make choices about the quality of the food we give our mind. Here, I am referring to a value judgment and this is where people don't always agree. For example, if you have the opportunity to go out for an evening and see a movie, what will you choose? What input do you want to give your brain? How do you want to feel when the movie is over? Will you choose a film which portrays violence, anger and a victim mentality, or one which personifies hope, laughter or joy?

In the spirit of self-nurturing, I suggest input activities which nourish your mind and spirit. Years ago, I made the conscious decision to change my mind-filling time and activities. I had to look at how I was utilizing my time. I also began to look at some emerging patterns of what I was currently doing and how it was making me feel. Like many Americans, I would begin my day with a cup of coffee and the morning news. News is primarily negative in nature - we all know this. In fact, the newspaper *USA Today* did a survey, collecting samples of all the news reported through all mediums (radio, print, television). They found that 95% of what is reported to the public is negative. This is no big surprise to any of us. Is our mind affected by this bombardment of our senses with negative words and images? Absolutely! This is the negative input I spoke of earlier. Negative stimuli (experiences) can create negative thoughts, feelings and actions. When we eliminate the negative experience, we create more room for the positive to come into our life.

In this process of learning to self-nurture, I eliminated many things which I perceived as negative or non-beneficial to my growth. For example, I eliminated most television-watching. As I fine-tuned my day and began to fill it with self-nurturing activities, I discovered that television-watching occupied a significant amount of time that could be better spent doing good things for me. Given the option, I substituted reading time for television time. I occasionally still watch television, but I choose carefully what I watch. I prefer to watch programs that sustain and nourish me, that make me feel good when they are over or help me to learn something new. Public television or the travel channel or any number of growth-oriented programs are available, once you seek them out. To me, mindless television-watching was a waste of my precious time. In keeping with this mode of self-nurturing, I also changed my reading, listening and film-watching habits. Moving away from violent, negative-themed mediums helped tremendously. I saw and felt an immediate shift when I chose to be very discriminating about movies, books and music. I had more energy, felt more enthusiastic and empowered.

Given a choice, why would we select to surround ourselves with negativity unless we truly enjoy feeling bad? It will again take time and attention on your part to courageously choose what will enable you to become your best self. The choices may be difficult and not understood or well received by others. Only you know what stimuli and experiences nurture you and which ones make you depressed, unambitious or unhealthy. Make the positive choice to give your mind bread - and while you are at it, choose whole wheat over white!

Programming for a Positive Day

Making the decision to change my mind-filling time and daily activities was an easy one. Developing the discipline to do so was something else altogether. I began with changing my morning routine. Instead of getting up and going directly to the couch with a cup of coffee to wake up and turning on the morning news, I chose to do something that sets a positive tone for my day. My morning routine may now involve an early morning walk, listening to music or twenty minutes of inspirational reading. I may also chose to sit quietly and reflect, gathering my thoughts for the day ahead.

This early morning time is crucial in setting the tone for your day. The first 30 minutes upon waking is prime time to feed your mind. Just arising from alpha sleep, we are highly suggestible. Choose carefully what you do in the first 30 minutes of wakefulness. Choose an activity that will allow your mind to gently awaken, and be filled with nourishment and sustained for the day ahead.

Your evening routine is equally as important. The 30 minutes before sleep is crucial for setting the tone of your rest and dreaming patterns. Researchers have shown that the stimuli you experience right before sleep can be repeated five to seven times per night in your dreams. If we seek peaceful restful sleep, it behooves us to choose pre-bedtime activities that do not over stimulate us or create tension or nervousness.

I have found it helpful to engage in what I call a nightly "de-tox" ritual. For 30 to 60 minutes before bedtime, I begin a wind-down routine. It involves slowing my physical pace, bathing or showering, listening to music or a guided relaxation tape or reading something motivational or inspirational. In short, I try to end my day on as peaceful a note as I begin my morning. Activities to avoid before bed would be watching the news, reading a newspaper or watching a violent television program or movie. These can cause our mind to switch into "active" mode, creating sleep disturbances and less than restful sleep. This 30 minute routine also gives the mind time to slow down. Often, as busy women, our pre-bedtime routine is spent busily scrambling to do the last minute things for tomorrow. We are still doing laundry or picking up the house or paying bills late at night. We slide into bed, our mind racing with unfinished business. Sleep doesn't come easily. With a 30-minute "de-tox" routine, our mind can gradually slow. Taking a few minutes to calm it (deep breathing is helpful here) and then filling it with something nurturing or restful, is beneficial. Try it, and see if you notice the difference - as I did. Thirty minutes in the morning and thirty minutes in the evening can give our body and mind the needed nourishment they need to grow.

Other Mind-Growing Activities

Our culture abounds with ways to grow our mind. We are surrounded with opportunities and resources that enable us to enrich our life daily. The only issues we are truly faced with are whether we have the time and the passion to incorporate new mind-expanding activities into our life.

I make the following recommendations to you for mind-growing activities:

- Take a class
- Learn a new skill
- Begin a new hobby
- Go to the theater, symphony or ballet
- Visit a museum or art gallery
- Go to the library
- Create a book list - read the books you never got to read when you were younger (Audio books are great, too)
- Create a music list. Listen to all the types of music you have never heard before

Take the time to create your own personalized wish list of activities you would like to do to grow your mind. All these things enable our mind to expand in awareness, to broaden the picture of where we are and what we can become. These things also nourish our soul. When the intellect is allowed to soar, so does our spirit. It is all interconnected, as we have already discovered. In attending to the needs of your mind, you attend to the needs of your spirit as well. Create a plan of action for yourself. One woman I met created a book list of over 50 titles she had never read - everything from *Moby Dick* to *Zen and the Art of Motorcycle Maintenance*. She is working through her list, crossing off each book title as she reads it.

I created a music list. I had been raised in a household filled with music, but it was primarily Big Band music and show tunes. When I began my self-nurturing regimen, I sought out classical music. I was not familiar with it, so I ventured to the local music store where I could buy bargain-priced classical music CDs (most libraries also have a large and varied selection of tapes and CDs). I started with Beethoven, Mozart, Tchaikovsky and Ravel. It was a fun adventure to become acquainted with these composers I had only heard of before. Their music was enriching and also provided much needed relaxation.

Acquiring new knowledge through any of the above-mentioned activities does much more for our self-nurturing than we admit. Learning something new boosts our self-esteem. We gain additional insights into ourselves and the world around us. Confidence builds as we acquire new skills and put new information into our personal databank. Challenging our mind enables us to move beyond self-limiting beliefs and helps us to remain open to new possibilities.

Make a commitment to yourself to spend at least 15 to 30 minutes each day, feeding your mind. Our mind is a very valuable gift and we nourish our entire self when we give it the time and attention it needs. An expansive mind will serve us faithfully into our older years.

Dorothy J. Hulst writes, "The world is your kaleidoscope, and the varying combinations of color which at every succeeding moment it presents to you, are the exquisitely adjusted pictures of your ever-moving thoughts."

Self-Nurturing Thoughts

Just as you may choose to grow the garden of your mind, you can also choose specific thoughts which help support your self-nurturing journey. We have already discussed the extraordinary number of thoughts we have each day. What if you took the time to specifically focus on your thoughts and send positive messages of self-nurturing to your body/mind? In *As A Woman Thinketh*, Dorothy J. Hulst explains, "If you would perfect your body, guard your mind. If you would renew your body, beautify your mind." By sending beautiful, loving thoughts to yourself, you can enhance your own growth process.

Louise Hay, respected publisher and author of *You Can Heal Your Life*, teaches about the power of our thoughts. She writes, "Whatever we believe becomes true for us. If we want a joyous life, we must think joyous thoughts. If we want a prosperous life, we must think prosperous thoughts. If we want a loving life, we must think loving thoughts. Whatever we send out mentally or verbally will come back to us in like form."

Be aware of the power of your self-talk. Your inner chatter will determine who you are and what you become. If you speak negatively to yourself, i.e., "Why did I do that? I am so stupid," we negate our sense of self and cannot move toward personal growth. If we speak positively to ourself, i.e., "I learn from my mistakes; I did my personal best," we move toward our best self. We need to be aware of the words we speak to ourself. Choose your self-talk carefully. Send verbal messages of love and acceptance to yourself.

Louise Hay also brought the concept of positive affirmations into the daily lives of millions of people. Affirmations are positive statements of belief we can say to ourself which reinforce positive behavior or outcomes. It is much more than wishful thinking, as some would claim it to be.

Affirmations can help us to focus our positive intentions and mental energy on our own healing process.

An example of an affirmation we could use for self-nurturing would be, "I deserve personal time to spend any way I see fit." Repeating this message out loud to oneself or writing it on a journaling page, creates a positive mindset. We then move toward that desired outcome. The opposite is also true. If we harbor thoughts of being selfish or unworthy, we will move in that direction. What we think about expands and we move toward that goal.

In creating affirmations it is important to word them in the first person, present tense, as if the action has already occurred. Another example would be, "I easily find time in my busy schedule for self-pampering rituals." Here are a few more examples of affirmations you can use to assist you in your self-care regimen:

- I serve my body well by eating healthy, nutritious food.
- I enjoy moving my body daily for energy.
- I feel more healthy each day.
- I take private, self-nurturing time without guilt.
- I love and honor my body.
- I listen to my body's wisdom and give it what it needs.
- My thoughts are my own and I choose them wisely.

What are your current issues on self-nurturing? Write them down. Create affirmations that help you reverse your thoughts about your situation. Put them on an index card or in your journal so you can read them several times per day. The first 30 minutes in the morning and the last 30 minutes at night before bed is the optimal time to speak your affirmations aloud. Giving voice to them gives them energy and speeds you in the direction of their fulfillment.

Expect that it will take up to 21 days for your affirmations to take hold. Studies have shown that it takes approximately 3 weeks to change a habit or thought process on any given thought. You can speed up this process by immediately initiating specific self-care activities. Giving action to these thoughts propels you forward in the direction of your goal.

If, deep inside yourself you know these affirmations to be untrue and utterly impossible, in all likelihood they will not come true. Firm belief and personal conviction are necessary for affirmations to work. Therefore, it is of utmost importance to create statements that are realistic and achievable.

Using affirmations that are positive and self-nurturing will enhance your healing process. Begin to send thoughts of love to yourself on a regular basis and you will be surprised how quickly your body, mind and spirit will respond. One of my favorite theories of affirmations by Louise Hay has to do with harnessing the amazing power of your mind to create a new you. In *Heal Your Life* she writes:

> In the infinity of life where I am, all is perfect,
> whole and complete. My life is ever new.
> Each moment of my life is new and fresh and vital.
> I use my affirmative thinking to create exactly what I want.
> This is a new day. I am a new me.
> I think differently. I speak differently. I act differently.
> Others treat me differently.
> My new world is a reflection of my new thinking.
> It is a joy and a delight to plant new seeds
> for I know these seeds will become my new experiences.
> All is well in my world.

"Flushing" the Mind

As crucial as it is to fill and expand our mind, it is also important to flush. By 'flushing' I mean taking the time daily to empty your mind - let it be still, calm and quiet. To do so is no easy task. Our mind is busy processing a cacophony of sounds, sights and smells each minute of every day. In fact, researchers tell us that we think approximately 60,000 thoughts per day. The chatter that incessantly drones on in our head adds to the confusion. It is easy to overload mentally. That is why it is so important to dedicate time each day, 15 to 30 minutes, to flush our thoughts.

Most of our day is spent living in our head. It takes concentrated effort to learn how to slow down our thought processes and arrive at a place of mental quiet. The practice of meditation is one which can help us do just that. Meditation is described by Sri Chinmoy, author of *The Wings of Joy,* as "going to the bottom of the sea where everything is calm and tranquil. On the surface of the sea, there may be a multitude of waves, but the sea is not affected below. In its deepest depths, the sea is all silence."

Meditation enables us to do more than quiet our mind. Individuals who regularly meditate experience lower blood pressure, slower respiration and longer brain wave patterns than in many sleep states. Studies have also shown that experienced meditators have lower cholesterol levels, lessen their need for many medications, show increased creativity and efficiency and have sharper memory. Meditation can also be used as spiritual practice, enabling one to go deep within to discover Life Truths. Once again, we find evidence of the intertwining of body, mind and spirit. Meditation practice, like yoga, enables one to bring balance to all three areas of ourself.

The practice of meditation is confusing to some who do not understand how it differs from prayer. Prayer is a form of communication which goes out from oneself to a Higher Power. It may be in the form of a request or words. Meditation, on the other hand, is a slowing of thought which goes inward. Sri Chinmoy writes, "When I pray, I talk and God listens. When I meditate, God talks and I listen. When we pray, we go up to God. When we meditate, God comes down to us."

Many misconceptions surround meditation as well. There are hundreds of ways and techniques to meditate. There is no one correct way. The key is to find one that works for you. Often it involves sitting quietly in one spot, using breathwork to facilitate the relaxation process. Sometimes a word or sound (a "mantra") is used to focus the mind and still the thoughts. However, meditation can also be engaged in while walking or even eating. No matter what technique you use, the important thing is to find time in your busy day - 15 to 30 minutes is recommended - to quiet the mind.

Meditation can be found in all religious and spiritual disciplines from Christianity to Buddhism. Jesus often spoke of taking time apart from the crowd to still the mind and connect with a Higher Source. He often did so Himself. The Buddha wrote prolifically of meditation practice. He taught His disciples "to awaken, sit calmly, letting each breath clear your mind and open your heart." That is literally the heart of meditation - moving from mental chatter to the whispers of your heart.

My meditation practice is not as disciplined or as time-consuming as others, but it works for me. While it is recommended that we meditate for 20 to 30 minutes daily, I find that to be difficult at this point in my life. However, it is something I hold in my mind's eye as a goal to be worked toward. For sitting meditation, spine straight with body relaxed, I find 10 to 15 minutes works for me. I feel immediate benefits. My mind is clear and relaxed. I am energized (even more so than with a nap). My senses are heightened and I experience a general sense of well being. Usually I focus on my breath to help me enter this deep state of meditation. Other times, I use a sound like "AH". The meditation I described in Chapter Two by Thich Nhat Hanh is helpful, too, "Breathing in, I calm my body. Breathing out, I smile. . ."

I offer this advice for beginning meditators:

- Select a quiet time and place.
- Let yourself sit upright. Feel as if your spine is directly anchored to the ground.
- Close your eyes gently.
- Allow yourself to become more and more still.
- Feel your breathing.
- Continue to relax and put your attention on each breath.
- After a few breaths, your mind may wander or be restless. Gently bring it back, returning to your breath.
- Try to achieve a state of mental quiet. When mental chatter increases, focus on your breath to clear your thoughts.
- Notice how your breath becomes shallow naturally as you move into a deeper state of relaxation.
- After you have sat for 20-30 minutes in this way, open your eyes and look around you before you get up. Take a few deep breaths to bring energy back into your body.

Meditation, for me, has been an invaluable tool in reducing stress and anxiety. It has enabled me to get in touch with a deeper part of myself than ever before. It has also enabled me to develop a deeper relationship with the Divine.

Another form of meditation which you may find valuable and easy to do is walking meditation. In *Buddha's Little Instruction Book*, Jack Kornfield states, "Walking becomes a meditation when we bring a careful present attention to each step we take. Walking becomes a meditation when we feel ourselves fully here on the Earth. . .The natural ease of walking can be used as a direct and simple way to bring centeredness and peace into our life. Walking meditation can be done by measuring out a space fifteen to thirty paces in length, walking with an awareness of breathing and foot placement. It can be done indoors or out."

I prefer to combine fast walking with walking meditation. I get my cardiovascular workout by walking with an awareness of breath and pace. It takes me to a place of non-thought and mental emptiness. It also brings mental clarity and heightens sensory awareness. As I walk on the beach near my house, I count my steps, creating patterns with inhales and exhales. I hear the birds overhead and the waves rolling onto the shore and

I savor the smells of the beach. If my thoughts wander, I gently guide them back to counting my steps and breath. For a comprehensive description of many walking meditation exercises, I recommend *Long Road Turns to Joy: A Guide to Walking Meditation*, by Thich Nhat Hanh.

Meditation can provide you with a sense of balance. Once again, we find a practice where body, mind and spirit can come together. Meditative practice has also gifted me another very important source of self-nurturing. When I give myself permission to be alone with myself, sitting or walking with no other agenda than to just *BE*, I feel valued and loved. I love and value myself enough to enjoy the quiet for as long as I need to. I feel at peace and at home with myself. J. Donald Walters writes in *Secrets of Meditation*, "The secret of meditation is affirming that you already *are* those high truths toward which you aspire: inner peace, Divine love and perfect joy."

~ ~

As you learn to harness the power of your mind, you will find the quality of your life improving. As you seek to fill your mind with positive experiences, you will notice not only a shift within yourself, but in those around you. Positive people and opportunities will come into your life. The sense of mental peacefulness you have achieved through meditation practice can imbue others with a sense of peacefulness as well. Indeed, as you change your mental landscapes, you can change your personal reality. As we learn to feed our mind we create a more positive world for one and all.

The Courage To Be Myself

I have the courage to...
Embrace my strengths--
Get excited about life—Enjoy giving
and receiving love—Face and transform
my fears—Ask for help and support
when I need it—
Spring free of the Superwoman Trap—
Trust myself—Make my own decisions
and choices—Befriend myself—Complete
unfinished business—Realize that I have
emotional and practical rights—
Talk as nicely to myself
as I do to my plants—Communicate
lovingly with understanding as my goal—
Honor my own needs—
Give myself credit for my accomplishments—
Love the little girl within in me—
Overcome my addiction to approval—
Grant myself permission to play—
Quit being a Responsibility Sponge—
Feel all of my feelings and act on them
appropriately—Nurture others because
I want to, not because I have to—
Choose what is right for me—Insist on being
paid fairly for what I do—

(continued on next page)

The Courage To Be Myself
(continued)

Set limits and boundaries and stick by them—
Say "yes" only when I really mean it—
Have realistic expectations—Take risks and
accept change—Grow through challenges—
Be totally honest with myself—
Correct erroneous beliefs and assumptions—
Respect my vulnerabilities—
Heal old and current wounds—
Favor the mystery of Spirit—
Wave good-bye to guilt—plant "flower,"
not "weed" thoughts in my mind—
Treat myself with respect and teach others
to do the same—
Fill my own cup first, then nourish
others from the overflow—
Own my own excellence—Plan for the future
but live in the present—Value my
intuition and wisdom—Know that I am
lovable—Celebrate the differences between
men and women—Develop healthy, supportive
relationships—Make forgiveness a priority—
Accept myself just as I am now--

Sue Patton Thoele
(reprinted with permission)

A woman is literally what she thinks—
her character being the complete sum of all her thoughts.
Dorothy Hulst

Whenever you are not active physically,
do something creative in your mind...
Creative thinking is marvelous—like living in another world.
Paramahansa Yogananda

Take time to think—it is the source of power.
Take time to read—it is the fountain of wisdom.
Author Unknown

Tell me what you pay attention to, and I will tell you who you are.
Jose Ortega Y Gassett

All the flowers of all the tomorrows are in the seeds of today.
Author Unknown

An untrained mind can accomplish nothing.
A Course in Miracles

If you can imagine it, you can achieve it.
If you can dream it, you can become it.
William Arthur Ward

The more I accept my mistakes as opportunities to learn,
the easier it is to pick up my wisdom and move on.
Joan Borysenko

(Wo)man's mind stretched to a new idea,
never goes back to it's original dimensions.
Oliver Wendell Holmes

When the student is ready, the teacher will appear.
From Buddhist Lore

The act of writing is the act of discovering what you believe.
David Hare

Far away there in the sunshine are my highest aspirations.
I may not reach them, but I can look up and see their beauty,
believe in them, and try to follow where they lead.
Louisa May Alcott

I dwell in possibility.
Emily Dickinson

So plant your own garden and decorate your own soul,
instead of waiting for someone to bring you flowers.
Veronica Shoffstall

If you are losing your leisure, look out!
You may be losing your soul.
Logan Pearsall Smith

There is no need to go to India or anywhere else to find peace.
You will find that deep place of silence right in your own room,
your garden, or even your bathtub.
Elisabeth Kübler-Ross

Be glad of life because it gives you the chance
to love and to work and to play and to look at the stars.
Henry VanDyke

Learn to be a radiant human and shine on others.
Sark

Unless you try to do something beyond what you have already mastered,
you will never grow...
Ralph Waldo Emerson

Nature does not demand that we be perfect.
It requires only that we grow.
Joshua Loch Liehman

CHAPTER 5

ENRICH YOUR SPIRIT

Let us realize the importance of slowing down, of taking the time to reconnect with this wondrous world of ours, our innerselves and this truly magical universe of which we are a part. Reconnect with that still, small voice inside each of us that guides us and helps to understand our purpose here. Take time to meditate, pray, reflect on the miracle of our being, the incredible beauty of our universe and being part of that plan. Will you sit back, relax, enjoy and be thankful for your life, your family and friends? Can you *BE*, instead of *DO*?

The Importance of Slowing Down

A recent errand into our local office supply store brought me face to face with its owner. I had had several conversations with him about my seminars and the work I was doing with women. Knowing I was always on the lookout for new resources, he announced, "I have got one for you." He scurried downstairs to his office, returning with a sign he had removed from his wall. Russ proceeded to say, "I know you speak to women about slowing the pace of their life and about self-nurturing and, truthfully, I'm tired of it. Men feel that way, too. We know we need to stop the crazy pace of our lives, but we don't know how. This is how I feel almost every day. Here. . .read this," and he shoved the paper into my hand. On it was the following:

> I'm lost. . .
> I've gone to look
> For myself.
> If I should return
> Before I get back,
> Please ask me to wait.
> Thank you.

I was pleased he shared this with me because this quotation certainly is indicative of what many of us are feeling today. In the hustle and bustle of our daily lives, we feel confused or lost, not knowing how to slow the roller coaster of life, but wanting to get off very badly. It seems impossible to slow down and find the time we need to truly enjoy life when there are bills to pay, deadlines to meet, kids to send off to college. The daily duties alone are enough to overwhelm us - much less the long-term goals and plans we are supposed to be moving toward. Many of us feel we are not living our lives - our lives are living us.

Previously I mentioned a euphemism coined by author Adair Lara in her book, *Slowing Down in a Speeded Up World.* She refers to us as "human doings," rather than "human beings," as the pace of life picks up and we feel we are rapidly losing control. We are caught up in the "doing" mode and have great difficulty learning to just "be." This constant doing mode can cause us to feel disconnected from ourself, the world around us and the Divine. We feel nervous, anxious, stressed, lonely, rushed, depressed. . . all these are symptoms of moving at a much faster and intense pace than we were intended to. Adair Lara writes,

> Everybody's life has speeded up. People used to spend months lolling on ocean liners, just getting to Europe, or 3 to 4 hours in a carriage, smelling the green fields while getting to town. Now we prowl supermarket aisles in search of minute meals, send clippings to friends instead of letters, rinse out panty hose while we are in the shower and wear jogging gear to the manicurist so we can take a 20-minute run while our nails dry.

The only solution to this frenzied cycle is to learn to slow down. And in the process of slowing down, we will be rewarded with the time we need to enrich our spirit.

By enriching spirit, I mean taking the time to reconnect with yourself, your purpose, the world around you, your spirituality and your God. Until we give ourself permission to get off the roller coaster and designate time and space for our spiritual work, we will continue to feel disconnected and overwrought. There is no time like the present. This can be the day you say to yourself, "I want to live my life fully instead of my life living me." Let us begin the final leg of our journey to wholeness together. Arm in arm, we stroll along the path which will lead us to the greatest wellspring of all, that of spirit. Our vessels we will fill with a greater sense of self and Higher Purpose. We are almost Home.

The Dilemma of the Past and Future

It is not an easy task to slow the pace of one's life. Why is it so difficult to let it all go, to give up the "doing-ness" and just "be?"

The first stumbling block that comes to mind is the societal value we put on effort. Achievement and goals are the hallmark of our mental processes. More, bigger, faster, best are the qualities we continually strive for. We place high value on those who work hard and excel. "Doing" is prized. "Being" is not. "Being" carries the societal implication of being lazy, careless, apathetic, even backward.

I ask you to consider a new definition of "being" so we may leave behind its negative implication. By "being," I mean being fully present in the moment - not worrying, not hurrying, not looking backward or forward. Whatever activity you are engaged in, whether it be performing a task at work, doing laundry, gazing at a sunset or eating an apple, you are fully aware and consciously experiencing that activity. Your mind is not wandering here or there. It is focused, enjoying the experience for what it is.

The Buddhist tradition calls this "mindfulness." We can describe it as living in the moment or being present-centered aware. When we are truly living in and for the moment, we have no sense of worrying or hurrying and we do not feel the stresses of life. Living mindfully is a lifestyle change that I will share with you in greater depth in the next few sections.

It is difficult for us to make the transition from doing to being (learning to live in the moment) because most of the time we are not in the present moment. Our body is here and now, but our mind is elsewhere. We are either thinking about the past or thinking about the future. The 60,000 thoughts we think each day are centered in what we could have done, just did, or will be doing. As we work the assembly line, drive the car, mow the lawn or prepare a meal, how often are we truly experiencing that unique and specific moment? Chances are, we are replaying in our head old tapes of conversations and events (and how we should have done it differently) or we are worrying about the future - what will happen in a few hours, tomorrow or beyond. We are rarely fully present with what we are doing at the moment.

An example from my personal archives: My son was 8 years old and not keen on competitive sports. I gave in to the pressure of other parents and forced him to play softball because "it would be good for him" and "to build character." He hated every minute of it and so did I. To sit on the bleachers for two hours when I had so much to do seemed like a waste of time. The innings were interminable (you know how few hits there are in pee-wee softball), and my thoughts continually wandered to the laundry pile at home, scores of business phone calls to return and the huge "To Do" list I carried in my head at all times. Finally, I was jolted to awareness only to see the ball rapidly rolling to the outfield and a boy standing on first base. I realized it was my son. In my preoccupation with the "could-haves" and "should-haves" I never saw my son's only hit in softball. Later, as he ran up to the stands, my heart sank. "Mom! Did you see my hit?" he shouted. "Of course!" I answered. "It was great!" But I didn't see it. I was not present.

How often have you experienced such events that found you mentally consumed by thoughts of the past or future? How many important magical moments have escaped you because "no one was home?"

Living in the present takes full effort and concentration. If you recall, in Chapter One we discussed four major stepping stones necessary to begin a program of self-care. These four stepping stones are necessary as well to slow the pace of our life. In review, they are:

- Giving Yourself Permission
- Giving Up Perfection
- Prioritizing for Personal Time
- Developing a Passion for "Me" Time

Each of these four steps will lead us to a new awareness in our daily routine that each moment can be fully savored and enjoyed. Each moment is special. The past cannot hold us. The future need not concern us. We are "home" whenever we are fully present.

For many of us, this awareness of the present becomes important only when we are faced with a tragedy of some sort. I spoke earlier of my "hit the wall" experience with my health which opened my eyes to a new way of being. If you have ever suffered a dramatic loss or death, or are dealing with a life-threatening illness for yourself or another, you know that the importance of living in the present makes itself known. The past is over and done with. There is no reason to dwell on the past except to learn from it and go on. We have no guarantees of tomorrow. We may not even be here 1 hour from now.

Barbara DeAngelis, Ph.D., has said in her book, *Real Moments*:

> Yesterday is history
> Tomorrow is a mystery
> Today is a gift
> That is why we call it the 'present'.

The present moment is truly a gift - a gift we can leave unopened and unenjoyed or one which we can joyously unwrap to savor its beauty and meaning. The choice is ours.

As we learn to take one day at a time, to revel in its sweetness and, yes, to fully experience the sorrows as well, we move to a place of wholeness. As we heighten our awareness of the uniqueness of each moment, we slow the pace of our life. Golden moments become golden hours.

To live in the present is to accept who you are today. As you give full attention to your daily activities, you will become more aware of your needs and feelings. To live in the present is, indeed, another form of self-nurturing. As we let go of past regrets and future worries, we validate ourself and who we are becoming. Our spirit is enriched.

"Be Here Now"

Sometimes it is necessary to engage in actual "mindfulness" exercises to help us become more focused on the present. I have already shared one technique in Chapter 2 that I use regularly, to focus in on myself for achieving a sense of calm. Rhythmic breathing, counting the in and out breaths, is a good way to focus in on the present. When we concentrate on our breath, all our thoughts about past and future dissipate and we are truly in the moment. Practicing your breathing while you are engaged in another activity can also heighten your awareness, whether it be bicycle riding, grocery shopping or changing a baby. Concentrating on your breathing can enable you to literally breathe new life into the activity you are engaged in. It helps you to focus and be fully participative.

When my life pace seems to have picked up once again and I feel myself getting out of touch with the present, I use an exercise that is Buddhist in origin to bring me back to the present moment. It pulls me out of my "doing" mode and brings me back into my "being" mode. I would like to share it with you. Wherever you are, no matter what you are doing, you can do this exercise:

> Take a moment and breathe in deeply and exhale deeply. Be aware of your breath - how it feels going in and out of your nose, in and out of your chest. Continue for a few breaths and mentally scan your body. How do your feet feel on the ground or floor? Traveling up your body, assess how your shins, legs and knees feel. If you are sitting in a chair, how does the chair feel? What does your body feel like, pressed into the seat and back of your chair? How do your arms feel? Are they pressed in tight to your body, or relaxed and loose? How do your hands and fingers feel? What about your shoulders? Are they hunched up or hanging loosely? How does your neck feel - stiff or loose?

> Beginning with your chin, scan your face and move up. Are your teeth clenched together or are your lips relaxed with mouth slightly open. Are your eyebrows scrunched together, or are they loose and wrinkle-free?
>
> Now, bring your awareness back to your breath and rescan your entire body. Be totally aware of how your physical body feels. Next, repeat to yourself the words, "Be here now." Fully engage all five of your senses. Be aware of each sound around you, the smells, any taste in your mouth. Turn up your senses to high volume and listen with your entire body. Fully feel what it is like to be you, in your body, in this exact time and space. No moment will ever be the same as this moment. Repeat again to yourself, "Be here now." Gradually bring your awareness back to center. If you have closed them, open your eyes and look around you.

You have now experienced what it is like to be fully present-centered aware. Time had no hold on you. There was only an eternal now. If you noticed, your body was relaxed and at peace with itself. Your mind was calm and peaceful as well. Your spirit was being enriched. You can carry this feeling with you wherever you go and recreate it any time. It is especially useful during times of stress or anxiety. Use it any time when you want to heighten your awareness and bring your attention to what is going on right in front of you. This exercise can be done with your eyes open so that no one needs to know you are doing it. It is an intensely private way to reconnect with yourself and the world around you.

To learn to live each moment fully aware does take practice. The exercise above will help. Yoga, spiritual movement and meditation will also help you and begin to enhance the vibrancy of your daily experiences. Paramahansa Yogananda writes, "Live each present moment completely and the future will take care of itself. Fully enjoy the beauty and wonder of each instance."

Sensory Awareness

Another way to achieve mindful moment-to-moment living is "paying attention on purpose." This involves learning to heighten our senses. In our society today, many of us experience sensory overload. There is too much stimulation, too much noise and, as a result, in an act of self-preservation, our senses shut down. We become numb or unaware of much of what is going on around us. We become desensitized.

I recall a period of a few years when my stress level was very high and the pace of my life was frenetic. I was trying to care for two preschoolers, a husband who worked 70 hours per week, two dogs and a career for myself. Much of the time I felt numb and on sensory overload. Only later did I realize that I had shut off my senses in an effort to create a pseudo-sense of calm in my daily life. I ate without tasting, lost track of nature and its seasons. Sights and sounds whizzed by without much recognition. Of course, I did not realize at the time that this was happening. Only later, as part of my "hit the wall" health experience and my personal spiritual awakening, did I realize what I had been missing.

I remember it was fall in Michigan. I was driving home from a class I had been taking, when I suddenly noticed the trees had turned color. I was shocked to notice them. The colors were vibrant - yellows, reds, oranges. "When did the leaves turn color?" I asked myself. That moment was a turning point. I looked around, and everywhere I looked the world was alive with color. It was as if the Master Painter had reached down with a paintbrush and filled a canvas with beautiful hues just for me. I was awe-struck. Only then did I realize how long I had been living in a gray world. I had not been aware of the beauty of nature for a long time.

From that moment on, my world changed. I heard birds singing again. I smelled new aromas and savored new tastes. Even my fingers longed to experience the feel of new textures. I reached out like a child to feel the soft green grass, the silky petals of a flower, the rough bark of a tree. My senses were exploding!

How long had I been gone? How long had I been so caught up in the busy-ness of life that I had become unaware of the world around me? In hindsight, I now realize it was almost two years. I give thanks to God for bringing me back to myself and my world.

Today my senses reel with aliveness, but only because I practice at helping them remain heightened. I have learned to pay attention to my senses and in doing so have given myself new eyes with which to see the world. We need to learn to pay attention, especially when there is so much to distract us from this process of becoming aware of the present moment.

An Exercise in Noticing

Allow me to share another series of exercises you can use to heighten your awareness and keep you connected to the beauty of the moment by using your senses. Our five senses are our window to the world. If they are dull or have been dormant for a while, they may need to be re-trained. Most of us have five senses that are fully operational, but the degree to which they are functioning may be questionable. If you have the gift of sight, how much do you really see? If you have the ability to taste, what do you truly savor?

The ideal place to practice heightening our senses is out of doors. Choose a spot where you will not be interrupted or too distracted.

> Let's begin with our hearing. For a moment, imagine you have been given a hearing device that can be adjusted higher or lower. Take a deep, centering breath and turn up your hearing device. Listen intently. What do you hear? Turn it up a bit louder. What do you hear now that you didn't hear before? Take a few moments and really listen with your two ears.
>
> Next, become aware of your sight. Imagine that you have been given a magical pair of glasses which, when you put them on, enable you to see things vividly and brightly. What do you see around you? What colors and shapes are right in front of you? On each side of you? Turn around and look behind you. Look up to the sky and down to the ground. Soak it all in. Take a deep, centering breath and turn your vision up a notch. What do you see now that you didn't see before?
>
> Now engage your sense of smell. Take a deep inhalation through your nostrils and notice what comes to mind. Are there odors or fragrances? What unique smells are in the air? Now, turn up your sense of smell and become aware of a new smell you didn't notice the first time. Breathe deeply and inhale these smells into the core of your being. Does this make you feel different? Do the smells affect your thoughts and emotions?
>
> Next, imagine you have been given a pair of invisible gloves that will bring a new sensation to your palms and fingertips. Put them on and imagine that the tips of your fingers are supersensitive, as if they have never touched anything before. Reach out and touch the object closest to you.

> How does it feel? Warm? Cold? Rough? Smooth? Run just your fingertips over it. Savor it with your fingers. Now use your entire hand, including the palm, to feel the object. Run your hand over it. Can you grasp it or place your hand around it? How does that feel? Move to a new object nearby and try the exercise again. How does this object feel?
>
> Last, become aware of your sense of taste. Bring your attention to your mouth. What taste is in your mouth right now? It is sweet? Bitter? Reminiscent of a recently consumed food or drink? Move your tongue around to explore the inside of your mouth. How does the roof of your mouth feel? The sides of your mouth? What do your teeth feel like, front and back? Explore. Slowly extend your tongue and move it over your lips. How do your lips feel? Can you feel their texture? Smooth? Rough? Dry? Moist?

As we practice this exercise over time for each of our five senses, we can begin to turn them up on demand. In my workshops, I like to take a sensory awareness break and send participants out of doors to complete this exercise. I may instruct them to go outside and select a small object (a pebble, a leaf, a blade of grass, a flower) to practice this exercise on. They harness each of their five senses and fully experience how that object looks, feels, smells, sounds like and tastes (if appropriate). They return to the room, object in hand - a newfound awareness intact. Interestingly enough, the object is often placed lovingly in front of them on the table or desk. It becomes a symbol of a newly acquired experience. Many participants take their object home as a reminder of their brief exercise in noticing. They say they feel an immediate change in their sense of well-being because their senses are fully functioning again.

It is also helpful to do this exercise while eating. Slowly move through each of the five senses and ask yourself what you notice about the food in front of you. Allow yourself to fully see, feel, smell, listen to and savor each morsel. Eating becomes a whole new experience when it is done mindfully. For thousands of years, followers of Buddhism have been engaged in practicing mindful eating. As a meditative practice, it allows one to focus totally on the present moment and to give appreciation for it as well.

"Noticing" takes practice. As life zooms by, many of us have gotten out of touch with what goes on around us. The auto-pilot mode that we find ourselves on doesn't allow us to take the time to truly see and feel our daily experiences. As we fine tune our senses, we begin to open up to a whole new way of being - but it takes practice.

As we finely tune our senses, we become more aware of the beauty around us - beauty that is found in the people, places and situations that are indeed right in front of our eyes. We are unable to see them for what they are until we clean the dust and dirt off our lenses to see more clearly. In the words of Marcel Proust, "The real voyage of discovery consists not in seeking new landscapes, but in having new eyes."

Reconnecting With Nature

As human beings, we belong to the animal kingdom and the world of nature, but many of us feel more "apart from" than "a part of" nature. We live and work indoors, away from our natural environment. We are surrounded by artificial light, noise and structures. Joan Arnold, writing for *New Woman* magazine (May, 1995), says:

> As our daily surroundings become more synthetic, we rush to work in cars or trains to spend our days in sealed climate-controlled boxes. With our senses numbed by a daily barrage of noises and images, few of us deem it crucial to watch the shape of the clouds or finger a leaf.

Is it a wonder, with this sort of daily regimen and exposure to unnatural surroundings, that we feel disconnected? If we pay attention to our body-mind-spirit response, we will notice that we feel at home in the natural world. We actually feel better when we are out-of-doors, breathing fresh air instead of processed air and soaking in the sights and sounds of Mother Earth. We may also notice a relaxation response that comes more quickly out-of-doors.

Arnold goes on to present a study by Bernadine Cimprich, Ph.D. which shows that exposure to nature can have a profound influence on our health, attitude and general well-being. She found that, "women recovering from breast cancer surgery fared better when they were closer to nature. . . In her study, patients were divided into two groups. Those involved in a nature activity three times per week for 90 days complained much less of mental fatigue or inability to cope. Compared with the control group, their cognitive acuity was measurably sharper, they were more likely to return to work full-time and were more game for new endeavors, like losing weight or learning to play an instrument."

Enriching our spirit though reconnection with nature involves two steps. The first is to "begin noticing," paying attention on purpose, as we discussed in the last section. How often have we been shocked to suddenly notice the beauty of a blue, cloud-filled sky or the deep green currents of a mountain stream? Fine-tuning our senses will help to diminish our separation from the world around us which comes from being caught up in the busy-ness of life.

The second step, however, is to give ourselves permission to set aside time for simply enjoying nature. Mother Earth beckons us each moment to come savor her delights, but do we heed her call? Richard LeGallienne writes, "I meant to do my work today, but a brown bird sang in the apple tree and a butterfly flitted across the fields and all the leaves were calling me." Spending time in nature allows us to slow the pace of our life and be present-centered aware. The cycles and rhythms of nature are slow. Time is not important. Nature calls to us to come and enjoy her. We can leave behind the stresses and strains of daily life and just BE. Mother Nature provides us with the perfect setting to do just that. Once again, we become one with nature. We are another creature in her majestic creation.

Leisure time spent in nature is truly restorative. In making positive choices for your self-care regimen, I recommend establishing "nurture me through nature" time. For myself, there is nowhere else where I feel more at home and at peace, than in the beauty of Mother Earth's domain. If you have the option of choosing a nurturing or enriching activity that can be done indoors or out, I recommend choosing out of doors. You will find that your relaxation response will come much faster than if you remain indoors.

Make a commitment to yourself to take precious time in nature. Reconnect with the earth that sustains you. Give thanks for its beauty and allow your spirit to soar as you witness its everyday miracles. Whether you notice a seagull flying high above the ground or you finger the velvety soft petals of a blossoming rose, allow yourself to be nurtured, fed and enriched by our first and forever Mother - the Earth.

Enjoying Solitude

When was the last time you gave yourself permission to be alone, to revel in the quiet and peacefulness of solitude? Jean Huston, author of *A Passion for the Possible*, writes, "It doesn't interest me where or with whom you have studied. I want to know what sustains you from the inside when all else falls away. I want to know if you can be alone with yourself and if you truly like the company you keep in the empty moments."

I know women whose lives have been on the fast-track for so long that when the opportunity for solitude time comes, they hardly know what to do with it. One friend who needed respite from a 50-hour work week took 3 days away from spouse and children to do exactly what she wanted to do. She packed her bags, got in the car and headed nowhere in particular. Before leaving, she confided in me that she wasn't sure she could handle 3 days all by herself. I could not imagine that she could not handle 3 days of what I would consider to be bliss. How delicious it would be to do nothing but nurture myself. Visions of long walks on empty beaches, browsing for endless hours through bookstores, savoring delicious gourmet meals, sleeping through the night with no interruptions. . .aah, that would be the life. She thought so too, until the time came to embark on her self-styled adventure. She was back home again after one day. Twenty-four hours of alone time was enough for her. Three entire days of being by herself seemed interminable to her. Because she was so used to being busy all the time, she found it extremely difficult to wile away the hours in a leisurely fashion.

I perceive alone time or solitude as encompassing two different types of activities for the purpose of self-nurturing. We have already spoken of one of these in Chapter Two, Finding ME Time - time to be alone, time to be spent on yourself in any way you see fit that nurtures you. A wide range of activities can be enjoyed during your ME time.

The second type of alone time is the one I refer to here - the opportunity to be alone with yourself and your thoughts amidst silence. If you are not used to spending time alone where peace and quiet abound, you may need mental preparation to do so. Solitude may take getting used to.

As much as we crave it, once we have it many of us are uncomfortable with the silence and lack of distractions. Baby Steps come in handy here. Yoga and meditation can pave the way for your alone time. Begin by giving yourself small increments of time to be alone so the silence is not deafening. I would suggest that instead of just sitting, use nature's bounty to get back in touch with the wonder of stillness. My best moments of solitude are found as I walk along a moss-covered path in the woods, senses keenly attuned, mental processes clear and devoid of chatter. You can begin your journey to solitude by sitting beside a babbling stream or at the edge of your blossoming garden or on top of a hill overlooking your neighborhood or city. Be aware of the stillness around you, breathe it in and let it bring you peace.

Begin with even a few moments of solitude each day to discover how much solitary time you require. Hopefully with time and practice, you will find that you crave progressively larger servings of solitude.

Being alone with ourselves provides us the opportunity to slow our outer world, to get in touch with our inner world. We need not go anywhere specific to find a sense of solitude. Renowned author, Elisabeth Kübler-Ross writes, "There is no need to go to India, or anywhere else, to find peace. You will find that deep place of silence right in your own room, your garden or even your bathtub."

Time dedicated daily to solitude can bring abundant blessings. One immediate result is a feeling of centeredness. As we breathe in the silence, we allow our body to rest, our mind to become calm and our spirit to be re-connected to the world around us.

In her book, *The Call of Solitude*, Ester Buchholz, Ph.D. writes, "Some people like to climb mountains to be alone. They need really dense isolation. We call these people loners, a term which has a stigma attached to it. Maybe we should call them soloists instead. The only way to learn how much solo space you need is by spending time alone and monitoring how you feel."

Solitude is a cornerstone of our self-care regimen. However, what each person hopes to gain from solitude will vary. For you, it may be peace and quiet - a welcome respite from the craziness of daily life. For another, it may be a time to breathe and relax. For some of us, the need for solitude goes even deeper. It is a time to reconnect with our inner self, to gain needed insights or to connect with a Higher Power. These things cannot be achieved without silence. Our thoughts must slow enough to make room for new insightful ones to come forward. I use solitude practice when I need answers. I go to a peaceful place, begin to concentrate on my breathing, quiet my thoughts. I may pose a question and in the stillness of the ensuing moments, wait for insights to make themselves known.

Within each of us are the answers to our deepest questions. Silence is the only way to access those answers. We have been conditioned to believe that the answers we seek to life's dilemmas are "out there somewhere." Nothing could be more untrue. The deepest wisdom lies within. Within silence are more answers and insights than we ever dreamed possible.

In solitude we can also take the time to reflect on our life - where we have been and where we are going. We can offer up thanks for our life, our family and friends. Use your solitude time to pray, meditate or reflect on the miracle of your being. You are a wondrous gift to the universe. Give thanks for the gift of *you*.

Seeking the Source

I once heard a story about an elderly woman who lay dying. She had spent 85 good, productive years on earth. Her grown son sat by her side, listening to her reminisce about her life. "You know," she said, "I always believed God had something special planned for me, but I never figured out what it was."

Have you taken the time to figure out where you fit in the Divine Scheme of things? I believe we are all here for a purpose. On our life's journey, if we take the time to be still and listen, we will discover our life's purpose.

When we take quiet time each day, time to let the silence enfold us, we give ourself the opportunity to connect with the Sacred. As we come to conscious adulthood, it is up to each one of us to seek a relationship with the Universe. None of us are here by accident. Where do you fit into the greater scheme of things? Abbess Hildegard of Bingen, a 12th-Century mystic, wrote, "At birth, our Divine Potential is folded up in us like a tent. It is life's purpose to unfold that tent."

In the spirit of self-nurturing, give yourself the time and opportunity to discover your Divine Potential. Until each of us knows why we were put on this planet at this exact moment of time, how can we live a truly authentic life? How can we live our life "on purpose?" As we truly love ourself into wholeness, we can recognize our talents and abilities and put them to good use.

In the *Seven Spiritual Laws of Success*, Deepak Chopra describes the Sanskrit term "Dharma" ("purpose in life") as the Divine taking human form to fulfill a purpose. "According to this law (Law of Dharma) you have a unique talent and a unique way of expressing it. There is something that you can do better than anyone else in the whole world." This is the same Divine Potential that Abbess Hildegard and hundreds of mystics and spiritual teachers have spoken of for centuries.

No one can tell you what your unique talent is. You must discover it for yourself. We discover it through trial and error, growth and through service to others. We can discover it by getting in touch with our Sacred Self. Through dedicated time, reflection and meditation, the answers can come. Prayer can also provide insights. Albert Einstein wrote, "I want to know God's thoughts. . .the rest are details." How true! Until we become aware of our Divine Purpose, how can we create wholeness within ourself? The biggest piece of the cosmic puzzle will remain missing. We can love ourself with unmatched passion, but if we cannot comprehend the Passion that created us, we will always be less than whole.

~ ~

In enriching our spirit, let us give ourself permission, time and the opportunity to slow the pace of our life, to reconnect with nature, to reflect and embrace solitude and to connect with our Divine Purpose. These are the final steps on our journey that will bring us to a new understanding of ourself.

Let the Pendulum Swing

Let the Pendulum swing.
Let the old guard surrender
It is a new day, a new world,
A new language I wish to speak
The language of love
May I have the words I need to speak my truth,
To translate my heart and my vision
To my beloved and his children
To all who come to sit at our table
Or walk with us through the market place
Or pray with us by the water

May I have the plain poetry to tell them how I feel
Or why there is pain,
If the answers are mine to know.
And if they are, I ask the Spirit to let me share them
With a light heart, with laughter,
With no expectation, with humility
But for the grace of Thee, go I.
Every moment of every day
May I be a child forever
Intoxicated by hot sand, cool winds, by love
By my own communication to the Spirit.
May my aliveness always be as loud
When I make love, as when I cry
May I see my own reflection in the mirror
And smile

Julia Loggins
(reprinted with permission)

When we have the first awareness of
'rediscovering our spirit,'
we know that there is someone there, inside of us,
who is well worth knowing.
Shakti Gawain

Whatever our souls are made of, yours and mine are the same.
Emily Brontë

It is good to have an end to journey towards,
but it is the journey that matters in the end.
Ursula LeGuin

Learn to get in touch within yourself and know that
everything in this life has a purpose.
There are no mistakes, no coincidences,
all events are blessings given to us to learn from.
Elisabeth Kübler-Ross

Forever remember that the business of life is not merely about business,
but about life.
B. C. Forbes

You will never 'find' time for anything.
If you want time, you must make it.
Charles Buxton

Happiness is a butterfly which when pursued is just beyond your grasp...
but if you will sit down quietly, may alight upon you.
Nathaniel Hawthorne

Understand that you are not a human being have a spiritual experience.
You are a spiritual being having a human experience.
Wayne Dyer

Live each present moment completely,
and the future will take care of itself.
Fully enjoy the wonder and beauty of each instance.
Paramahansa Yogananda

I meant to do my work today, but a brown bird sang in the apple tree, and a butterfly flitted across the field, and all the leaves were calling me.
Richard LeGallienne

Inside myself is a place where I live all alone and that's where you renew your springs that never dry up.
Pearl S. Buck

I want to know if you can be alone with yourself,
and if you truly like the company you keep in the empty moments.
Jean Houston

The real voyage of discovery lies not in finding new landscapes,
but in having new eyes.
Marcel Proust

You have to sniff out joy.
Keep your nose to the joy trail...
Buffy Saint-Marie

This is what one thirsts for, I realize, after the smallness of the day,
of work, of details, of intimacy—even of communication,
one thirsts for the magnitude and universality of a night full of stars,
pouring into one like a fresh tide.
Anne Morrow Lindbergh

At birth our divine potential is folded up in us like a tent.
It is life's purpose to unfold that tent.
Abbess Hildegarde of Bingen

There is only one time when it is essential to awaken.
That time is now.
The Buddha

The golden opportunity you are seeking is in yourself.
Mary Engelbreit

When you perceive yourself as spirit,
you will not simply feel love—you will be love.
Deepak Chopra

Welcome to sunrise in paradise.
Kenny Loggins

CHAPTER 6

PUTTING BODY, MIND AND SPIRIT TOGETHER FOR BALANCE

In each of the last chapters, you learned how and why it is important to nurture yourself. You have a deeper understanding of how to give your body, mind and spirit the attention they deserve. You know that you need to do good things for yourself and certainly desire to do so. Yet one obstacle remains - where do you find the time you so desperately need to self-nurture?

~ ~

A quote from Charles Buxton can provide further assistance in easing our dilemma. He says, "You will never 'find' time for anything. If you want time, you must make it." There will never come a day when you have more time. Each day contains the same 24 hours, the same challenges and obligations. Most likely, there will never be a time in your life when you are less busy or feel less overwhelmed. Even in retirement, many individuals say they are busier than ever. It is a matter of choice. If you truly desire to make the necessary changes in your life which will further your growth process, you will have to take the time.

Let's recap and summarize how much time we are talking about here. In each of the last three chapters, I gave a daily time recommendation for each area:

Nurture Your Body:

Movement	15 minutes
Self-Pampering	15 minutes
Healthy Eating	(no set time requirement)

Feed Your Mind:

Fill With Positive Input	15 minutes
Flush for Mental Quiet	15 minutes

Enrich Your Spirit:

Reflection	Time commitment optional
Living in the Moment	Requires change in perception
Reconnecting With Nature, Self and Spirit	Can be done in combination with body and mind activities

I would consider the above to be a minimum recommendation. However each one of you know realistically what you can and can't do for yourself right now. Beginning a program of self-care requires a time commitment each day. If you engaged in each of these prescribed activities for 15 minutes each day, you would be dedicating a total of only *1 hour per day to yourself.* In the greater scheme of things, that is not much time out of a 24-hour day. Aren't you worth it? From a broader perspective, we are worth much more than that. If 15 minutes for one of the above activities seems impossible, start with 5 minutes and increase the dedicated time over the next few weeks.

Be aware that it is not necessary to begin dedicating time in all three areas at once. Choose one area to which you would like to give immediate attention. Do you recall that we spoke of Baby Steps? Here is where we put them to work. The point is not to overwhelm you, but to encourage you to make the commitment to get started *today*, so that the transition to self-care is a gentle one. If you put pressure on or overload yourself to do too much too quickly, this program may seem like a burden. Remember this process of becoming self-aware is for your Highest Good and only has your positive growth in mind. Give yourself permission to create a self-nurturing schedule, one that you look forward to each day and that is doable and reasonable.

Begin by taking a few moments to complete the following exercise provided here, entitled "Where Will I Ever Find The Time?" Take a typical day in your hectic life. Fill in the blanks, hour by hour, with your daily activities. I am aware that your days may vary but choose one typically busy day and fill in the time slots. I have provided a completed schedule as an example. ***Fill in your schedule on the next page.***

WHERE WILL I EVER FIND THE TIME?

EXAMPLE

AM	6:00	Get up/dress. Awaken 2 children. Get to bus by 6:45.
	7:00	7:30 Awaken 3rd child. Get to bus by 8:30
	8:00	Get myself ready/shower
	9:00	Leave for yoga class (On alternate days I fast walk)
	10:00	Yoga class for 1 hr.
	11:00	Go to work
PM	12:00	Work at Center/Store (no lunch break)
	1:00	At work
	2:00	At work
	3:00	Leave work to pick 1 child up for her job
	4:00	Home to pick 3rd child up from bus
	5:00	Nap/prepare dinner/go over homework/do laundry/dishes
	6:00	6:30 Leave for class
	7:00	Class from 7-9 PM
	8:00	Class
	9:00	Home around 9:30/more dishes
	10:00	"De-tox" bath, reading time
	11:00	Asleep
AM	12:00	

WHERE WILL I EVER FIND THE TIME?

AM	6:00	______________________
	7:00	______________________
	8:00	______________________
	9:00	______________________
	10:00	______________________
	11:00	______________________
PM	12:00	______________________
	1:00	______________________
	2:00	______________________
	3:00	______________________
	4:00	______________________
	5:00	______________________
	6:00	______________________
	7:00	______________________
	8:00	______________________
	9:00	______________________
	10:00	______________________
	11:00	______________________
AM	12:00	______________________

Next, go back through your time slots and find the places where you can eliminate what you may consider unnecessary or postponable activities. Then, re-evaluate the time slots and find the places where you could add 10, 15 or 30 minutes of time *just for you* - to nurture your body, feed your mind and enrich your spirit.

If you have difficulty doing this, I would suggest completing the exercise with a friend. Fill out your schedule, give it to him or her for analysis. Often a person who is emotionally unattached to your daily schedule can help you see things that you cannot (like unnecessary activities, "wasted" or empty time, time slots that could be used more effectively). Chances are, like most busy women, you will find that your early morning and late evening time slots may be the only ones with some flexibility. Getting up earlier is an option and is a particularly good time for movement activities. Late evening time can be re-allocated. Maybe you can eliminate some television-watching time for other self-nurturing activities.

It is more difficult to find open time for yourself during the day. If you get a lunch hour at work, reassess how you are using that valuable 30 to 60 minutes. Could it be spent doing something enriching, like reading or going for a walk? I like to recommend to women to use their lunch hour (at least a few times per week) to go on a date with themselves. Instead of sitting in a workplace employee lunchroom, create an adventure for yourself. Take yourself on a date and explore a gallery, walk in the park, sample the wares of street vendors. Vary your routine to give you extra energy and something to look forward to. Variety, I believe, is the key to making a success of this self-care program. We all have the potential to get bored easily. Choose different types of activities and mix your week up with them. Refer to the Self-Nurturing Assessment Survey in Chapter 1 to get new and different ideas.

Be flexible in arranging your self-care schedule. One of the techniques that works best for me is to mentally rehearse in the morning what my day feels like. If it feels too busy or overwhelming, I immediately take stock, look at my schedule and figure out how I can change it to make me feel more comfortable. I will mentally run through my day, crossing off or postponing an activity to give me more personal time. An example: If my afternoon feels rushed and I know I have to teach a class at night, I will choose to pick my youngest child up at school. Why? If I pick her up, I am home 45 minutes earlier (than waiting for her bus to arrive) and I can use that 45 minutes to rest before heading back out to work in the evening. There are days when I may cancel entire mornings or afternoons, if I feel I need more personal time. This may seem nearly impossible for you to do now, but if you have truly worked through the steps outlined in Chapter 1 - Permission, Give up Perfection, Prioritize, and Be Passionate About Me Time - you will discover this process gets easier and easier.

Do "schedule" your Me time. Without actually writing it down and placing it on a calendar, you will risk not getting it done.

Be firm in carrying out your newly found self-nurturing routine. It is normal to receive resistance from those around you as you begin to take more time for yourself. As you grow and change, they will be forced to change also. Don't be surprised if your family, friends and co-workers seem to need you more than ever. Be aware that this is a normal process and that unconsciously they may be fearful of losing the *you* that they know and love.

In trying to find the balance between work, family and personal needs, I am reminded of a cartoon strip my mother sent me in the mail a few years ago. It showed the character, Lois (of *Hi and Lois*) busily doing her chores for the family. Frame by frame, she moves through her day; picking up the house, baking cookies, gathering up the laundry, doing the wash, grocery shopping, car-pooling to ballet classes. We also see that Lois is a working mother now. In the next frame, we see her dressed in a suit and high heels, heading out the door. As Hi and the children sit on the couch watching television, Lois announces, "Dinner is on the table. I have to go show a house. I'll be back in an hour." As the rest of the family sits at the dinner table, one child pipes up to say, "Boy! Mom hardly ever has time for *us* anymore!" Even though Lois has spent the bulk of her day attending to the needs of her family, they feel neglected as she goes off to work. If Lois adds self-care to her daily routine, they may miss her even more.

As you begin to take time to care for your own needs, others around you may indeed feel neglected. Remain passionate about your Me time and keep in mind that everyone benefits in the long run from your self-care regimen. Your new-found dedication to your own health and well-being is also an excellent example of role-modeling for them. Your good example may have a positive impact on those around you, and they may choose to follow in your self-aware footsteps.

I have also included in these pages, another tool to assist you in making the transition to self-nurturing. It is called a Weekly Minder. Use this chart to keep a record of your body, mind and spirit activities. By writing down your accomplishments each day, you will stay self-motivated and proud of the progress you are making daily to achieve a balanced life.

WEEKLY MINDER

(B) Body, (M) Mind, (S) Spirit

Monday	(B)	____________
	(M)	____________
	(S)	____________
Tuesday	(B)	____________
	(M)	____________
	(S)	____________
Wednesday	(B)	____________
	(M)	____________
	(S)	____________
Thursday	(B)	____________
	(M)	____________
	(S)	____________
Friday	(B)	____________
	(M)	____________
	(S)	____________
Saturday	(B)	____________
	(M)	____________
	(S)	____________
Sunday	(B)	____________
	(M)	____________
	(S)	____________

Each day, record the good things that you are doing for yourself in each of the three areas. You will notice beside each day of the week, there is a B for Body, M for Mind and S for Spirit.

At the end of the week, look back over your activities and note your progress. Assess how you did. Pay attention to where you still need improvement. Most importantly, reward yourself for doing a good job. By week's end, give yourself an immediate reward for sticking to your body/mind/spirit activities. Choose whatever your heart desires and gift it to yourself because you have earned it.

~ ~

You can find the time to do good things for yourself, but it takes determination and persistence. I am reminded of the words of Robert Collier, "You can have anything you want - if you want it badly enough. You can be anything you want to be, have anything you desire, accomplish anything you set out to accomplish - if you will hold to that desire with singleness of purpose. . ." Hold firmly to your vision of the self-aware life and rededicate yourself daily to your personal journey to wholeness.

CHAPTER 7

YOUR INNER LIGHT WILL SHINE BRIGHTLY AGAIN

Do you feel like you have found yourself again? Is your world brighter, clearer, full of vivid color? Do you see more smiles, eyes twinkling and human kindness? Some of you may be hearing the birds sing for the first time in a long time. The rain's delicate patter, the wind in the trees, the smell of fresh grass may all appear novel. If so, you have reconnected. Welcome back!

Is your inner light shining again? Do you feel energized and alert, yet calmly at peace with yourself? Isn't it wonderful? This is the way it was meant to be. Now you are on your own path. It will take some work to keep you there, but as you daily practice nurturing your body, feeding your mind and enriching your spirit, it will become easier and a matter of habit. Your inner light is shining again. I can see it and it is beautiful - just like you!

~ ~

The sense of wholeness we have been journeying to is not a destination to be reached. It is a process. The process of growing and coming to know who we are and what we need is life-long. Dag Hammarskjöld was correct in his perception of this when he wrote, "The longest journey is the journey inward." It is the longest journey we will ever take - and the most difficult.

The most amazing thing happens however, when we sink to the depths. We find what it is that we are truly made of. We discover our strengths and talents and a new sense of self. Simone Weil writes, "If we go down into ourselves, we find that we possess exactly what we desire." We can emerge from the depths of our soul and proudly announce, "I had it all the time. I am proud of myself and my growth."

I was reminded the other day of how long my process of journeying to wholeness has been and the depth to which it has taken me. My son was looking through a large pile of old photographs that were never organized into a photo album. He pulled out a Polaroid snapshot, gave it a puzzled look and passed it to me. "Who is this?" he asked. I held that photo and looked into the eyes of the person staring back at me. My heart dropped like a rock into the pit of my stomach. I knew that woman in the photo very well. At the time this picture was taken, she had just returned from a family vacation in California. Beside her stood a little boy, proudly displaying his first surfboard. His face radiated pure pleasure - hers portrayed pain. Her shoulders sagged as if the weight of the world was upon them. Her lips were tightly drawn. The most disturbing part of the photo, however, was her eyes. They were lifeless. Her eyes were sunk into hollow cheekbones with dark circles underneath. It was as if no one was home inside this human form. Yes, I knew her well. She was me.

"Who is it?" my son asked again, as he took the photo from my hand. I replied with a slight knowing smile, hints of tears at the corner of my eyes, "It is me." Incredulously, my son looked back and forth from my face to the face in the photo. "No, it's not," he said and he put the picture back in the drawer and walked away.

Looking at that photo taken 10 years ago brought back all the memories of the pain I was in at the time - the physical challenges caused by stress, the feeling of being overwhelmed and out of touch, but most deeply, the feeling of being unheard and invisible.

I gazed at the photo and continued the conversation with myself in an empty room. "You're right, son," I said. "That's not me. That is someone else and that woman is gone. And in her place stands the new me I have created."

My children are older now and truly do not know that woman of 10 years ago. Rarely did I let her emerge. The warm, caring, fun-loving mother of their childhood is who they remember. It was important to keep up appearances. It was important then for me to protect them from my pain.

Today, it is important to live an authentic life. It is vital for you and for me to boldly embark on our journey and to speak our truths. This is how we come to wholeness.

Jane Evershed, South African poet and artist, writes in her poem entitled *Truth Visiting*:

. . .Be Prepared
To risk everything you hold precious
For the truth inside you.
TRUTH IS EMPOWERING.
And to speak the truth is to
Overcome the fear of death.
And on the other side of Hell
Lies PARADISE.

~ ~

We have begun our journey to wholeness together and Paradise beckons to us. Stay true to your path, my friend. Do the work. Be gentle with yourself. Nurture and love yourself as if you were your only child.

You will not continue on this journey alone. Although our ways may seem to part as this book comes to an end, my thoughts and love will remain with you, as will the support and encouragement of many other women journeying homeward.

EPILOGUE:

THE JOURNEY HOME

Today is a glorious day! I have rearranged my schedule to give myself a morning of self-nurturing. As I walk the path that leads to the beach, my senses come alive. The beach is solitary - not a soul around except for the Soul of the Universe speaking to me, "Come. Enjoy."

It is late February in Michigan. Usually a bitter wind would be blowing and passage to the beach would be difficult. There are no icebergs on the lake this year. Our winter has been unusually mild, but also unusually dreary with lack of sunshine.

It is early morning and the sun begins to peek its way out from behind the clouds. The waves crash softly on the shore. A few seagulls make their voices heard. The sand is hard, making it easy to walk on. We had a slight frost last night and the surface of the beach glistens like diamonds. Looking closer, I see it *is* diamonds; the frost has laid itself out in diamond-like patterns on the sand. The fog begins to roll in and the view down the coastline is reminiscent of a Japanese brush painting. The sand dunes rise majestically out of the early morning fog. I think it would be a lovely adventure to walk into it, the fog's arms embracing me.

As I walk the shoreline, more and more sunlight comes, lifting the fog and carrying it away to different shores. Now the fishing boats have come. They glide along the surface, hoping to lure little creatures from their sleepy, comfortable depths. A host of seagulls bob lightly on the blue-green water. They wait patiently for tasty fish morsels to surface. Everything smells so fresh this morning! I can sense the coming of spring because the air smells alive. Can we actually smell things beginning to grow?

My pace quickens and my breath matches my steps. One in-breath, 6 steps. One out-breath, 6 more steps. The pattern of my breathing allows my mind to still. Looking down where I carefully plant each step, I spy beach treasures: the zebra mussel shell clusters, a sadly decomposing fish, uniquely shaped driftwood. I come upon an enormous tree stump washed upon the shore, its gnarly roots reaching out to the sky. What a beauty it is! I wish I could bring it home with me, but it is destined to roll in and out with the waves and find its final resting place somewhere else.

It is time to head back to the house. As I turn back, I decide that I will write reflections on my beach walk. I notice one last time the markings the waves leave on the beach this morning. The waves gently quiet and leave scalloped lines on the sand. These lines are beautiful to the eye. As the wave comes, it deposits its essence on the sand, leaving a fine, arched line. It recedes and the next wave does the same, but leaves its mark just a little bit differently. Its mark is a little higher or lower, wider or more narrow.

I am reminded that we are very much like the waves. We each leave our mark on this world and each one is very different, yet the same. We each strive to leave our mark and one is not more valuable than another. It is *our* mark. It records our journey.

It seems that like the waves, we go in and out, back and forth. We always return home to the shore, no matter how far out to sea we go. Deep out at sea, the waves roar. They swirl, rise to heights of 10 feet and more. Cold and darkness may prevail. They are challenged by strong currents and gusty winds. They are tested for their strength and endurance. Like us, the waves persevere because the shore beckons. There, at the shore's edge, they get to rest a little and become gentle rollers. Going in, going out, a little at a time, catching their breath. The shore is always the destination - home, a place to recoup, energize or rest. A place to touch base with oneself and others. It seems that the waves journey out and come home to themselves, just as we do.

As I walk back up the path to my house, I feel a tugging at my heart strings. It would be nice to stay longer at the beach. Sometimes I almost dread going back to this house made of wood and stone. It carries so many responsibilities and makes many demands on me. It would be so much easier to stay at the shore, being soul-fed by Mother Nature. But real life calls. It is time to leave my beach meanderings. My day will pick up pace in a few hours. Things will be hectic again - children to pick up, errands to run, business phone calls to return, dishes, laundry, a class to facilitate tonight. I will drop exhausted into bed later, I am sure, but for now my life has been enriched by my morning stroll.

At the beach my soul has been nourished. My well has been filled and I can go about the business of my day knowing that I took good care of myself today. Reflecting on the journey and taking the time to write about it has been wonderful. I feel in balance - like my body, mind and spirit are fully functioning together in perfect harmony. I am grateful for the lesson the waves taught me today. I thank Spirit for gifting it to me. My spirits are high and my outlook positive. I feel whole. I feel at home with myself.

I slow my steps to savor these magical moments a bit longer. I turn and gaze once again at the shoreline. I think of all of us who are on this journey to wholeness together. This is it. Our time has come. A gentle melody comes to mind. I am reminded again of the lovely words of welcome sung by Kenny Loggins in his song of the same title. It seems he sings them specifically for me and for you. "Please celebrate me home."

And I say the same to you, my friend.

"I celebrate you home."

Thank you for sharing the journey with me.

A Special Message to Women Healing From Breast Cancer

Dear Friend,

Four years ago when I created my first project, a motivational journal for women, entitled *How Does Your Garden Grow?: Lessons in Self-Nurturing*, I had no idea I would be sharing my work with women healing from breast cancer. I knew very little about this disease and knew very few women who had experienced it. I created that initial project on self-nurturing for women, like myself, who were leading overwhelming lives and struggling with self-care.

At the time, I did not make the connection between healing from breast cancer and self-nurturing until a young woman named Peggy Baker came into my life. Peggy is a social worker and is the Program Director for Oncology Support Services at University of Chicago Hospitals. In her travels, she had picked up a copy of my journal. She immediately called to tell me that the journal would be a wonderful tool for her to use with women who had breast cancer as a way of helping them express their feelings and experiences.

In the meantime, I was meeting more and more women who were healing from breast cancer. I began facilitating a women's healing circle; more women healing from breast cancer came to our circle, providing me with deeper insights into this unique healing challenge. I began to wonder why I was being pulled in this direction. . .why articles and books on breast health kept coming to my attention. Was there a connection between the message of self-nurturing I was sharing with women and healing from breast cancer?

Not until I read *Anatomy of the Spirit* by Carolyn Myss, and Christiane Northrup, M.D.'s works on women's illnesses and the mind-body connection, did the light go on. *I realized the manifestation in our physical world for nurturing (and the need for self-nurturing) was the female breast.* I now knew that Spirit had led me to do my lecturing and writing on self-nurturing for all women, yet also for a special segment of the population - women healing from breast cancer - so their journey to wholeness could begin.

It follows that if we as women are challenged by an illness which can ravage our breasts - our breasts being a universal symbol for love, sustenance and nurturing - *we can facilitate our own healing by nurturing ourselves back to wholeness*. Yes, even healing from breast cancer can be enhanced and accelerated with the self-nurturing principles I have outlined in this book.

It is now being documented and proven by the scientific community that dietary changes, exercise, stress reduction, slowing the pace of our life, joining a support group and even journaling, can speed the healing process and improve longevity. I do believe that the core messages found in this book - self-love and engaging in daily activities that nourish body, mind and spirit - will, in time, be proven to be central to our healing processes - even from breast cancer.

As this book goes to print, Dean Ornish, M.D., has released a landmark book, *Love and Survival: The Scientific Basis for the Healing Power of Intimacy*. He writes, "I am not aware of any other factor in medicine - not diet, not smoking, not exercise, not stress, not genetics, not drugs, not surgery - that has a greater impact on our quality of life, incidence of illness and premature death from all causes than the healing power of love and intimacy". Self-love and intimacy, of course, are key factors here.

If you are to heal, my friend (and remember - healing occurs on many levels: physical, emotional and spiritual), take the messages in my book to heart. Your healing journey from cancer can be enhanced by the steps I have outlined here. As I write this, University of Chicago Hospitals continue to utilize this book/journal with women diagnosed with breast cancer. Peggy Baker, LCSW, ACSW, shares, "This journal is a wonderful tool that encourages women to nurture themselves and understand their needs. It helps them focus on what is really important in their lives and pursue those things that bring them joy".

If you have had a mastectomy and lost a breast to cancer, it is crucial that you embark on a self-care program that brings wholeness to your body, mind and spirit. Experiencing such a procedure can indeed make you feel less than whole, but as we have discussed in these chapters, wholeness is a state of mind. Self-nurturing can be a path to such healing. Even though your physical body may not feel "whole," your authentic self can feel more whole than ever before. It will be up to you to seize the day and begin your own personal journey to wholeness. It can be done!

I would like to take this opportunity to share with you another excellent resource for self-healing. My good friend, Terry Bienkowski, C.H., has created an audio cassette tape series for women entitled, *Into the Heart of Breast Cancer*. It embodies the principles we have shared here and offers unique insights into breast cancer. The tapes focus on women's healing stories and the mind-body connection in recovering from breast cancer. She has also created guided meditations for healing on all levels as well as dealing with the fear of getting breast cancer or having a recurrence. This is ground-breaking work. Part of the proceeds of each sale go to breast cancer research. You may contact her at:

Terry Bienkowski, C.H.
P.O. Box 207
Ferrysburg, Michigan 49409
Telephone: 616.285.5515

I have been blessed to share this time with you, my friend. I wish you well on your journey. Please feel free to contact me to share your personal stories or resources, that we may pass them on to other women who are on the path to wholeness. If you wish to write or purchase autographed copies of my book, please contact me at:

Jan Forrest
Heart To Heart Press
P.O. Box 215
West Olive, Michigan 49460
Telephone: 800.341.5541

Namasté,

Jan

Bibliography & Recommended Reading & Listening

Angelou, Maya, *Phenomenal Woman*, Random House, 1994.

Brady, Janeen, "*Someone Special—You!*" (music cassette and booklet), Brite Music, 1992.

Breathnach, Sarah Ban, *Simple Abundance*, Warner Books, 1995.

Buchholz, Ph.D., Ester, *The Call of Solitude*, Simon & Schuster, 1997.

Canfield, Jack and Hansen, Mark Victor, *Chicken Soup for the Soul*, Health Communications, Inc., 1996.

Chinmoy, Sri, *The Wings of Joy: Finding Your Path to Inner Peace*, Fireside Press, 1997.

Chopra, M.D., Deepak, *The Path to Love: Renewing the Power of Spirit in Your Life*, Harmony Books, 1997.

The Seven Spiritual Laws of Success: A Practical Guide to the Fulfillment of Your Dreams, New Word Library, 1994.

Ageless Body Timeless Mind: The Quantum Alternative to Growing Old, Harmony Books, 1993.

DeAngelis, Ph.D., Barbara, *Real Moments*, Delacorte Press, 1994.

Domar, Ph.D., Alice D. and Dreher, Henry, *Healing Mind: Healthy Woman: Using the Mind-Body Connection to Manage Stress and Take Control of Your Life*, Henry Holt Books, 1996.

Dyer, Dr. Wayne, *Manifest Your Destiny: The Nine Spiritual Principles for Getting Everything You Want*, HarperCollins, 1997.

The Awakened Life, Nightingale-Conant Audio, Chicago.

Real Magic: Creating Miracles in Everyday Life, HarperCollins, 1992.

Frankle, Ph.D., Lois P., *Kindling the Spirit; Acts of Kindness and Words of Courage for Women*, Health Communications, Inc., 1994.

Gerzon, Robert, *Finding Serenity in the Age of Anxiety*, MacMillan, 1997.

Hanh, Thich Nhat, *Long Road Turns to Joy: A Guide to Walking Meditation*, Parallax Press, 1996.

Living Buddha, Living Christ, Riverhead Books, 1995.

Hay, Louise, *You Can Heal Your Life*, Hay House, 1984.

Hulst, Dorothy J. (transcribed by), *As a Woman Thinketh*, DeVorss Publishing.

Kornfield, Jack, *Buddha's Little Instruction Book*, Bantam Books, 1994.

Lara, Adair, *Slowing Down in a Speeded Up World*, Conari Press, 1994.

Larson, Jo Ann; Cole, Artemus, *How Do You Want Your Room...Plain or Padded? Sanity Preserving Tactics for Today's Woman*, Deseret Book Company, 1995.

Lindberg, Anne Morrow, *Gift From the Sea*, Pantheon Books, 1983.

Loggins, Kenny and Julia, *The Unimaginable Life: Lessons Learned on the Path to Love*, Avon Books, 1997.

"The Unimaginable Life: Lessons Learned on the Path to Love" (music), Columbia Records, 1997.

"Leap of Faith" (music), Columbia Records, 1991.

Louden, Jennifer, *The Woman's Comfort Book*, Harper Publishing, 1992.

McWilliams, Peter, *Love 101*, Prelude Press, 1995.

Ornish, M.D., Dean, *Love and Survival: The Scientific Basis for the Healing Power of Intimacy*, HarperCollins Publishers, 1998.

Phillips, Jan, *Marry Your Muse: Making A Lasting Commitment to Your Creativity*, Quest Books, 1997.

Popkin, Dr. Michael, *"Active Parenting"* (audio), Brite Music, Inc., 1989.

Roth, Gabrielle, *Sweat Your Prayers: Movement as Spiritual Practice*, Tarcher/Putnam, 1997.

Rupp, Joyce, *Dear Heart, Come Home: The Path of Midlife Spirituality*, Crossroad Publishing Company, 1996.

Schaef, Anne Wilson, *Meditations for Women Who Do Too Much*, HarperCollins Publishers, 1990.

Skog, Susan, *Embracing Our Essence: Spiritual Conversations with Prominent Women*, Health Communications, 1995.

Steinem, Gloria, *Revolution from Within: A Book of Self-Esteem*, Little, Brown Publishing, 1992.

Taylor, Robert; Seton, Susannah; Greer, David, *Simple Pleasures: Soothing Suggestions and Small Comforts for Living Well Year Round*, Conari Press, 1996.

Thoele, Sue Patton, *The Woman's Book of Spirit*, Conari Press, 1997.

The Woman's Book of Confidence, Conari Press, 1997.

The Woman's Book of Courage, Conari Press, 1996.

Walsch, Neale Donald, *Conversations With God: An Uncommon Dialogue: Book 2*, Hampton Roads Publishing, 1997.

Walters, J. Donald, *Secrets of Meditation*, Crystal Clarity Publishing, 1997.

Watson, Ph.D., Donna, *101 Simple Ways to be Good to Yourself*, Publications Services, Inc., 1993.

Zinn, Jon Kabat, *Wherever You Go, There You Are*, Saint Martins Press, Inc., 1994.

Acknowledgments

First and foremost, I thank Spirit for guidance and giving me the opportunity to speak my truth and for being with me every step of the way through the completion of this project. I am truly blessed and grateful.

I offer heartfelt thanks to the following people who made this project possible:

To my family, for their patience as I continue this journey to my best self. Thank you for sticking with me through thick and thin. I love you all!

To an amazing woman, Bonnie Herman Zachary, who created the beautiful artistic rendering that became the cover of this book. I honor your talent and creative genius. Thank you so much for joining me in this project. The best is yet to come!

To Michael Zachary for his generous efforts to co-create the book cover with no rewards or accolades. Thank you, Michael, for your support.

To Terry Bienkowski for your always open heart and attentive listening ear as I labored through these pages. Oh, the places we will go!

To Cathy Caldwell for the use of her wonderful poem and for teaching me how to breathe again.

To the Godivas for your unflagging enthusiasm and encouragement. Thanks for the play and laughter.

To my sweet sister of the soul, Linda, who first shared Kenny Loggins' beautiful music with me. Thank you for doing so. My life has never been the same.

To Mary Jacobs for the Divine Guidance you tap into and share with me to keep me on my path. Thank you for being there for me.

To Tracy McCasey for her invaluable editing assistance and Lori Schirf and Laura Bedford for their typesetting expertise.

To Lori Schirf, Fairy Godmother Extraordinaire. Thank you for believing in my dream and making it come true. I am blessed to have you as my friend.

And extra special thanks to the following people for their inspiration:

Sue Patton Thoele - your written words have given me much inspiration and guidance and "*The Courage to be Myself.*"

Kenny Loggins - your spiritually inspired lyrics and music have sustained me on my journey and continue to play inside of me as I take this next "*Leap of Faith.*"

Wayne Dyer - your words of wisdom and journey to enlightened living have given me the strength and passion to "*Manifest My Destiny.*"

God Bless You All!

About The Artist

Cover artist Bonnie Herman Zachary speaks of her personal healing journey:

When Jan asked me to design the cover for her book, I was both flattered and excited. Later, as the reality of the subject matter sunk in, I became overwhelmed with various emotions. Her projected publishing date of May 1998 would be exactly fifteen years since I was diagnosed with breast cancer, a topic that, until recently, was submerged in the far reaches of my past reality.

Creating the artwork became a clarifying and healing opportunity for me—a kind of closure. The concept of the new Venus (Aphrodite) opening up to herself, to her own inner wisdom, came to me in many meditations.

It is clear that we need to open up to our own inner voice and have confidence in our own choices—to trust the wisdom of our choices. We need to know that all the events in our lives are on purpose and recognize them as opportunities for growth. We need to keep adjusting to the changes that life brings our way and allow experience to happen.

When I was going through my cancer, I shifted into battle mode. I became determined. It was my wake up call to become the person I had always envisioned myself to be. My therapy choice came easily and clearly to me. I felt guided by the Universe. I never doubted that I was on the path I needed to be on. There was always the delicate balance between defiance and surrender, between denial and acceptance. It was an acceptance at a very profound level; it was an acceptance of the challenge laid out for me. I simply did the only thing I could do, and that was to follow my belief in natural holistic healing. For that intense and brief period of my life, I was invincible.

Now, fifteen years later, I can still tap into that energy, that knowing—that the power is there always—non-judgmental—waiting to be tapped into. Life's profound gift. The gift of knowing.

More About The Artist

Bonnie speaks about her art:

I find great joy in celebrating the primitive spirit of the feminine using celestial and mythological themes in my painting. My work has become a reflection of my own personal journey while honoring the creative expression in all of us.

Artist Bonnie Herman Zachary lives in Spring Lake, Michigan with her husband and their two daughters.

She can be contacted at:

Art From the Heart Studio
PO Box 206
Spring Lake, Michigan 49456

About The Author

Jan Forrest offers unique insights into the struggle we are all engaged in; to succeed and, also, find joy and tranquillity in life. As a true woman of the 21st century who is indeed trying to do it all, just like the rest of us, Jan shares the strategies she has used to be successful in her personal and professional life.

Coming Home to Ourselves: Journaling to Wholeness is a follow-up to her first project: a motivational journal and audiocassette entitled ***How Does Your Garden Grow? Lessons in Self-Nurturing***. She is a much requested speaker and workshop leader. Her topics include: *"Taking Care of Business and Me," "Stop Rushing and Start Living"* and others which focus on finding balance in a fast paced world.

Jan is also Co-founder and Director of The Gathering Place, a learning center for personal growth and conscious living in Grand Haven, Michigan. She lives with her husband and their three children in Michigan.

Jan loves to hear from her readers
about their personal journeys.

<u>You may write to her at:</u>

Heart to Heart Press
PO Box 215
West Olive, MI 49460

For further information on
Jan Forrest's motivational keynotes,
workshops and seminars, call:

Heart to Heart Press
800.341.5541